Homework Book

G000293591

MyMaths
for Key Stage 3

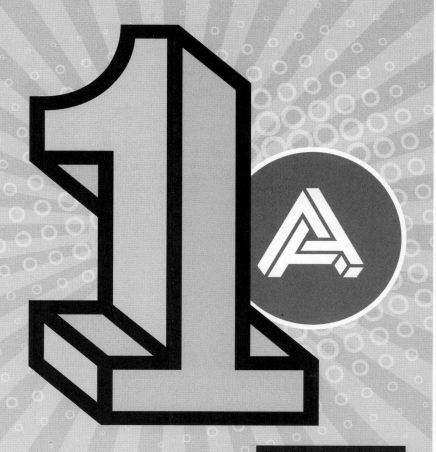

1A

OXFORD
UNIVERSITY PRESS

OXFORD
UNIVERSITY PRESS

Great Clarendon Street, Oxford OX2 6DP

Oxford University Press is a department of the University of Oxford.
It furthers the University's objective of excellence in research, scholarship,
and education by publishing worldwide in

Oxford   New York

Auckland   Cape Town   Dar es Salaam   Hong Kong   Karachi
Kuala Lumpur   Madrid   Melbourne   Mexico City   Nairobi
New Delhi   Shanghai   Taipei   Toronto

With offices in

Argentina   Austria   Brazil   Chile   Czech Republic   France   Greece
Guatemala   Hungary   Italy   Japan   Poland   Portugal   Singapore
South Korea   Switzerland   Thailand   Turkey   Ukraine   Vietnam

British Library Cataloguing in Publication Data

Data available

ISBN 9780-19-830444-9
10 9 8 7 6 5 4 3 2 1

Printed in Great Britain

Paper used in the production of this book is a natural, recyclable product
made from wood grown in sustainable forests. The manufacturing process
conforms to the environmental regulations to the country of origin.

Contents

What does each digit stand for in this number?

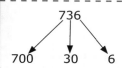

736

700   30   6

1 Lewis has three number cards.
   Using all three cards make

   | 3 | | 7 | | 4 |

   a The smallest number you can
   b The largest number you can
   c A number that is between the largest and smallest.

2 What does each digit stand for in these numbers?
   a 947   **b** 287   **c** 176
   d 3086   **e** 3604   **f** 4005

3 Copy the grid. Write the numbers
   as digits on the grid.

Hundreds	Tens	Units

   a Three hundred and twenty-seven.
   b Two hundred and ninety-one.
   c One hundred and fifty.
   d Three hundred and six.

4 Look at the table. Write each number in words.

	Thousands	Hundreds	Tens	Units
a	6	2	0	3
b		9	1	0
c	5	2	7	6
d	2	0	5	1

5 What does the underlined digit stand for in each number?
   a 43<u>5</u>   **b** 16<u>9</u>   **c** <u>7</u>06
   d <u>4</u>608   **e** 63<u>2</u>4   **f** 8<u>0</u>07

Write these numbers in order. Start with the smallest number.

a   15, 12, 18, 19, 11   **b**   29, 35, 21, 38, 42

- -

a   11, 12, 15, 18, 19   **b**   21, 29, 35, 38, 42

1   Write the numbers that are shown on the number line.

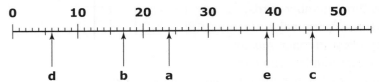

2   Write these numbers in order. Start with the smallest number.
   a   44, 35, 33, 43, 45, 34   **b**   97, 88, 98, 87, 99, 89
   c   231, 213, 123, 321, 132, 312   **d**   576, 756, 657, 567, 765, 675

3   Write these numbers in order. Start with the biggest number.
   a   57, 75, 65, 56, 76, 67   **b**   31, 23, 13, 21, 12, 32
   c   433, 344, 443, 343, 334, 434   **d**   676, 767, 677, 776, 766, 667

4   Copy and complete these using the greater than symbol (>) or the less than symbol (<).
   a   5 ☐ 3   **b**   4 ☐ 7   **c**   10 ☐ 8   **d**   15 ☐ 7

5   Write the names of the girls in order of height, starting with the tallest.
   Anne 145 cm   Candace 141 cm
   Dawn 143 cm   Rajmeet 150 cm
   Shani 146 cm   Mary 139 cm

6   This signpost is near Oxford. Write the towns in order of distance, starting with the nearest.

Burford 14
Cheltenham 30
Banbury 25
Birmingham 68
Newbury 30
Southampton 67

⬤ **MyMaths**.co.uk

Q 1217   SEARCH

What does each digit stand for in this decimal number?

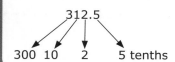

300 10   2   5 tenths

1 Write the decimal numbers that are shown on the number line.

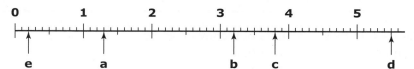

2 Insert the greater than sign (>) or the less than sign (<) between each pair of numbers using the number line in question **1**.

    a 3.4 ☐ 4.3   **b** 4.6 ☐ 3.9   **c** 1.7 ☐ 2.2

    d 1.4 ☐ 0.7   **e** 5.2 ☐ 5.0

3 What does each digit stand for in these numbers?

    a 637.2 **b** 75.3 **c** 38.9 **d** 245.8 **e** 520.2 **f** 600.3

4 On a grid like this, write these numbers as digits.

Hundreds	Tens	Units	•	Tenths	Hundredths
			•		

    a Twenty-four point five

    b One hundred and forty-five point three

    c Four hundred and twenty-five point four

    d Five hundred and twenty point nine

5 Look at the table. Write each number in words.

	Hundreds	Tens	Units	•	Tenths
a	3	5	6	•	4
b		8	4	•	7
c		6	8	•	3
d	4	3	0	•	8

Ian has two 10 pence coins, one 50 pence coin and one 20 pence coin.
How much does he have altogether?

Add
        0.10
        0.10
        0.50
    +0.20
        0.90   He has 90 pence.

1 Write each of these amounts of money in words.

   a £0.60   **b** £0.30

   c £0.80   **d** £1.50

2 Write each of these as a decimal.

   a sixty pence   **b** one pound

   c forty pence   **d** ninety pence

3 Add these amounts.

   a £0.20 + £0.20

   b £0.60 + £0.30

   c £0.90 + £0.10

   d £0.50 + £0.20

   e £0.20 + £0.30 + £0.10

   f £0.10 + £0.40 + £0.50

4 Lewis has four 5 pence coins, three 20 pence coins and
one 50 pence coin. How much does he have altogether?

5 Corinne has a 50 pence coin, two 20 pence coins and three
10 pence coins in her purse.
How can she make up these amounts?

   a £0.60

   b £0.40

   c £1.00

MyMaths.co.uk

Add these amounts of money.

a £0.20 + £0.80 + £0.50   **b** £0.25 + £0.11 + £0.05

a   0.20
    0.80
 +0.50
 £1.50

b   0.25
    0.11
 +0.05
 £0.41

1 Write each of these as a decimal.
   a twenty pence and six pence
   b fifty pence and two pence
   c three pence
   d ten pence and eight pence

2 Add these decimals.
   a 0.2 + 0.5   **b** 0.4 + 0.4
   c 0.1 + 0.7   **d** 0.8 + 0.2
   e 0.3 + 0.4   **f** 0.9 + 0.2

3 Add these amounts of money.
   a £0.20 + £0.30
   b £0.40 + £0.15
   c £0.50 + £0.55
   d £0.18 + £0.31
   e £0.15 + £0.40
   f £0.65 + £0.22
   g £0.20 + £0.45 + £0.10
   h £0.62 + £0.20 + £0.05

At 6 a.m. the temperature was −3°C, by 12 noon it was 5°C, but by 6 p.m. it was −1°C. Find

a the rise in temperature during the morning

b the fall in temperature during the afternoon.

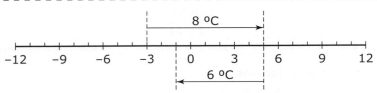

a Rise in temperature = 3 + 5 = 8°C

b Fall in temperature = 5 + 1 = 6°C

For questions **1** and **2** copy and complete the table.

1

	Starting temperature	Rise in temperature	New temperature
a	−2°C	7°C	
b	−6°C	4°C	
c	−3°C		2°C
d	−8°C		−5°C
e		9°C	6°C
f		5°C	−4°C

2

	Starting temperature	Fall in temperature	New temperature
a	5°C	8°C	
b	6°C	7°C	
c	4°C		−3°C
d	3°C		−5°C
e		8°C	−6°C
f		6°C	−2°C

3 One week in London the temperatures at midday were:

Monday 2°C, Tuesday −1°C, Wednesday 1°C, Thursday 3°C, Friday 0°C, Saturday −3°C and Sunday −2°C.

Rearrange these temperatures in order starting with the warmest.

MyMaths.co.uk

Q 1069   SEARCH

Example

Estimate the answer to 126 + 32.

---

126 rounds up to 130 (to the nearest 10).
32 rounds down to 30.
130 + 30 = 160

1 Round each number to the nearest 10.

a	8	**b**	23
c	78	**d**	51
e	102	**f**	99
g	234	**h**	615

2 Round each number to the nearest 100.

a	316	**b**	485
c	632	**d**	97
e	922	**f**	163
g	250	**h**	54

3 Estimate the answer to these calculations.

a	123 + 67	**b**	29 + 32
c	147 − 62	**d**	51 × 8
e	62 × 9	**f**	97 ÷ 19
g	546 + 82 + 21	**h**	53 + 11 − 18

MyMaths.co.uk

Q 1003, 1373 **SEARCH**

Calculate 32 + 51 × 4 − 102

- -

Multiplication or division must be done before addition or subtraction,
so 32 + 51 × 4 − 102 = 32 + 204 − 102 = 134

1 Work out these calculations.

a	12 × 3 + 11	**b**	7 + 14 × 2
c	1 + 95 ÷ 5	**d**	54 + 45 ÷ 9
e	9 × 6 − 7	**f**	15 × 4 − 12
g	16 × 4 − 20	**h**	9 × 7 − 17

2

a	8 + 12 × 7 + 6	**b**	12 + 15 × 3 + 9
c	13 × 6 + 7 − 29	**d**	2 × 18 − 64 ÷ 4
e	32 × 5 − 6 × 21	**f**	24 ÷ 8 + 9 × 7
g	85 + 171 ÷ 9 − 26	**h**	91 + 32 ÷ 8 − 43

3 Zodia and Zeek are picking apples in an orchard.
Zodia picks 15 apples each from 2 trees.
Zeek picks 12 apples each from 3 trees.
How many do they pick altogether?

4 Marcus is selling raffle tickets. He calls at one house and sells 2,
but at the next house 3 people come to the door and buy 4 each.
If he sells another 3 at a third house how many has he now sold?

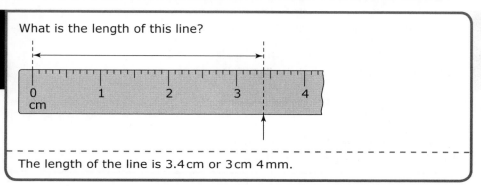

What is the length of this line?

0 cm   1   2   3   4

The length of the line is 3.4 cm or 3 cm 4 mm.

1 What is the length of each line?

   a |————————|

   b |————————|

   c |————————|

2 What are the three side lengths for each triangle?

   a   **b**

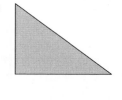
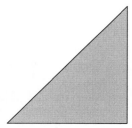

   c   **d**

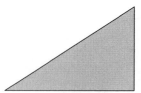

3 Draw these lines accurately.

a 8 cm	**b** 11 cm	**c** 12 cm
d 7.5 cm	**e** 10.6 cm	**f** 9.6 cm

What are the arrows pointing to on this scale?

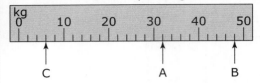

The scale is divided into 2 kg divisions.
A is 32 kg, B is 48 kg and C is 6 kg.

1 What are the arrows pointing to on each scale?

a

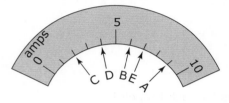

b

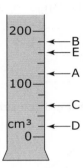

c

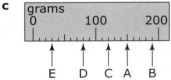

d

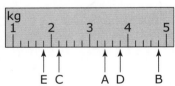

e

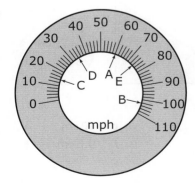

The clock shows a time in the early evening. What would a digital clock show for the same time?

The clock face is showing 6:15 p.m.
A digital clock would show 18:15.

1 For each of these times, write the numbers that a digital clock would display. All of the times are in the morning.

a

b

c

d

e

2 For each of these times, write the numbers that a digital clock would display. All of the times are after midday.

a

b

c

d

e

For this shape, write
a the number of sides
b the name of the shape
c the side lengths
d whether or not the shape is regular.

- -

a Three sides   **b** Triangle   **c** 17 mm, 17 mm, 24 mm
d Not regular, because the three side lengths are not the same.

For each of these shapes, write
a the number of sides
b the name of the shape
c the side lengths
d whether or not the shape is regular.

1

2

3

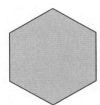

4

5

6

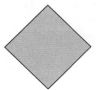

7

MyMaths.co.uk

Q 1229, 1390 **SEARCH**

What is the perimeter of this shape?
Use a ruler.

- -

The perimeter is 6 + 2 + 6 + 2 = 16 cm.

1 What is the perimeter of each shape?

a

b

2 What is the perimeter of each shape?

a

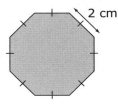

2 cm

b

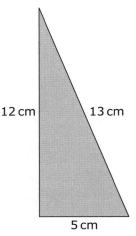

12 cm   13 cm

5 cm

c

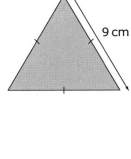

9 cm

3 Which of the shapes in question **2** are regular polygons?

Give the area of this rectangle by counting squares.

- -

14 squares = 14 units²

1 Give the area of each shape by counting squares.

a **b** 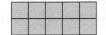 **c**  **d**

e **f** **g**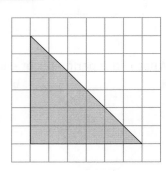

h 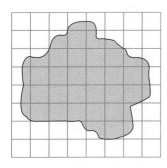 **i**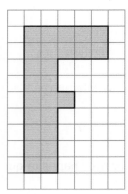

MyMaths.co.uk

Q 1084 SEARCH

John walks 850 m when taking his younger brother to school and then a further 2150 m to his own school. How many kilometres does he walk altogether?

Total distance = 850 + 2150 = 3000 m   Add the distances.
                      = 3 km   1000 m = 1 km

1   Which unit would you use to measure

    a   the distance from London to Manchester

    b   the mass of a dog

    c   the amount of tea in a mug

    d   the weight of a paperclip

    e   the amount of water in a bathtub

    f   the thickness of a piece of paper?

2   Fill in the missing information.

    a   10 mm = ____ cm

    b   100 mm = ____ cm

    c   100 cm = ____ m

    d   1000 m = ____ km

    e   1000 g = ____ kg

    f   1000 ml = ____ litres

3   At Fairtown Beach there is a miniature railway as shown on the map.

950 m	1800 m	1250 m
West Pier	Pleasure Park Swimming Pool	East Pier

    How many kilometres is it from East Pier to West Pier?

4   A party-size bottle of lemonade contains 3 litres.
    How many 150 ml glasses will it fill?

A writing pad has *p* sheets of paper.

Miles tears out 5 sheets.

How many sheets of paper are left in the writing pad?

- -

p sheets of paper −5 sheets of paper = *p* − 5 sheets of paper

1   In a book of stamps there are 10 stamps altogether.
How many stamps are there in
- **a**   3 books
- **b**   6 books
- **c**   *x* books?

2   A loaf of bread has *n* slices.
Alex eats 4 slices.
How many slices are left?

3   A milkman uses crates which each hold 15 cartons.
How many cartons can he put in
- **a**   2 crates
- **b**   4 crates
- **c**   *m* crates?

4   A packet contains *x* mints.
How many mints are there in the picture?

5   There are *n* people on a train but 25 get off at a station.
If nobody gets on, how many people are on the train now?

Write the number which is
a 20 more than x **b** y less than 25   **c** 10 times greater than z.

a $x + 20$ **b** $25 - y$ **c** $10 \times z$ or $10z$

1 Write the number for each of these.
   a 10 more than x **b** 8 less than z
   c u less than 9   **d** q more than p
   e b less than a **f** 5 times greater than x

2 There are p people waiting at the bus stop. After five minutes
q more people arrive.
   a How many are waiting now?
         Before the bus comes a further r people arrive.
   b How many people board the bus?

3 There are m passengers on a train.
At a station 20 more people get on and none get off.
   a How many passengers are on the train now?
         At a second station 10 people get off and nobody gets on.
   b How many passengers are still on the train?

4 Selva is knitting a sweater.
The pattern says she needs k balls of wool for size 1,
and two more balls for size 2.
   a How many balls of wool does Selva need to knit a
         size 2 sweater?
   b How many balls would she need to knit 2 size 1 sweaters?
   c Selva buys 18 balls of wool and knits 2 size 1 sweaters.
         How many balls does she have left?

Add the like symbols together.

a $b + 5b + 6b$

b $6x + 4y + x$

- -

a $b + 5b + 6b = 12b$

b $6x + 4y + x = 7x + 4y$

1 Add like symbols in each of these.

a $m + m$	**b** $p + p + p + p$	**c** $a + 2a$
d $c + 5c$	**e** $6y + y$	**f** $2t + 3t$
g $4v + 6v$	**h** $8n + 3n$	**i** $4b + 10b + b$
j $4m + m + 7m$	**k** $2z + 3z + 7z$	**l** $3x + 4x + 11x$

2 Add the like symbols together.

a $2x + 5y + 4x$	**b** $4a + 2b + 5a$
c $5u + 3v + 2u$	**d** $2m + 6n + 5m + 3n$
e $2u + 5v + u + 3v$	**f** $4c + 7d + 3c + 2d$
g $3x + 4y + 5x + 2y$	**h** $8m + 4n + m + 3n$
i $8u + 11v + 4u + v$	**j** $3r + 5s + 2r + s$
k $p + 4q + 9p + 3q$	**l** $5x + 6y + 8x + 2y$

3 Write an expression for the perimeter of each of these shapes.
Add the like symbols together.

a **b** **c** **d**

e 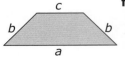 **f** **g** **h**

Simplify the expression $15m + 12n - 10m - n$

$15m + 12n - 10m - n = 15m - 10m + 12n - n = 5m + 11n$

1   Subtract like symbols in each of these.

a	$5x - 3x$	**b**	$8z - 3z$	**c**	$12m - 3m$
d	$9p - p$	**e**	$5r - 4r$	**f**	$2u - u$
g	$6b + 2b - 3b$	**h**	$7d + 4d - 5d$	**i**	$8p - 3p - 2p$
j	$12r - 6r - 2r$	**k**	$9t - 5t - t$	**l**	$10v - 6v - 3v$
m	$9a - 5a - 4a$	**n**	$14p - 2p - 3p - 4p$	**o**	$16v - 8v - 4v - 2v$

2   Simplify these by adding or subtracting like symbols.

a	$5u + 4v - 2u$	**b**	$8p + 9q - p$
c	$9c + 4d - 6c$	**d**	$10r + 5s - 2r$
e	$8b + 9c + 4b - 2c$	**f**	$11a + 12b + a - b$
g	$7x + 9y + 5x - 4y$	**h**	$8m + 5n - 7m + 3n$
i	$10u + 8v - 4u - 3v$	**j**	$7x + 5y - 4x - 2y$
k	$15a + 9b - 6a - 4b$	**l**	$18u + 8v - 6u - 7v$
m	$15c + 12d - 8c - 9d - 3c$	**n**	$11a + 16b - 2a - 4b - a - 6b$

3   On a supermarket shelf there are $7m$ bags of plain flour and $4n$ bags of self-raising flour.

a   How many bags is that altogether?

Mrs Singh buys $3m$ bags of plain flour and $2n$ bags of self-raising flour.

b   How many bags are left on the shelf?

4   A baker's delivery man has four trays on his van: one with $6x$ white loaves on it, one with $3x$ white loaves on it, one with $6y$ brown loaves on it and one with $2y$ brown loaves on it.

a   How many loaves is that altogether?

He calls at a factory canteen and delivers $4x$ white loaves and $3y$ brown loaves.

b   How many loaves are left on his van?

If $p = 7$ and $q = 4$, find the value of $3p + 2q$.

$3p + 2q = 3 \times 7 + 2 \times 4 = 21 + 8 = 29$

1 If $a = 15$, find the value of these.

    a $a + 7$ **b** $3a$ **c** $a + 6$ **d** $\dfrac{60}{a}$ **e** $a - 5$

2 If $b = 20$, find the value of these.

    a $4b - 15$ **b** $2b - 20$ **c** $100 - 2b$

    d $150 - 3b$ **e** $\dfrac{b}{4} - 3$ **f** $8 - \dfrac{b}{10}$

3 If $c = 25$, find the value of these.

    a $\dfrac{100}{c} - 2$ **b** $10 - \dfrac{75}{c}$

    c $\dfrac{80}{c - 5}$ **d** $\dfrac{40}{30 - c}$

4 If $m = 6$ and $n = 2$, find the value of these.

    a $4m + 3n$ **b** $8m - 5n$ **c** $8m - n$

    d $10n - m$ **e** $m \times n$ **f** $m \div n$

5 If $a = 5\,$cm and $b = 7\,$cm, find the perimeter of each shape.

a

b

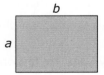

c

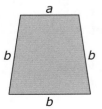

d

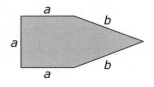

A calculator's battery compartment holds 2 identical batteries.

a Write a formula for the number of batteries a number of calculators would need.

b Find the number of batteries for
  i 5 calculators   **ii** 8 calculators.

- -

a number of calculators × 2 batteries = total number of batteries

b **i** 5 calculators × 2 = 10 batteries
  ii 8 calculators × 2 = 16 batteries

1 A type of light fitting has sockets for 6 bulbs.
  a Write a formula for the number of bulbs needed for several of these light fittings.
  b Find the number of bulbs that would be used with
    i 3 light fittings   **ii** 5 light fittings
    iii 12 light fittings   **iv** 15 light fittings.

2 A party can contains 4 litres of lemonade.
  a Write a formula to work out the number of litres any number of cans would hold.
  b Find the number of litres that would be contained in
    i 3 cans   **ii** 4 cans
    iii 5 cans   **iv** 12 cans.

3 A restaurant has 4 chairs round each table.
  a Write a formula for the total number of chairs in the restaurant.
  b Find the number of chairs needed for
    i 12 tables   **ii** 16 tables   **iii** 24 tables   **iv** 28 tables.

4 A forest is being cleared and each wagon can carry away 25 logs.
  a Write a formula for the number of wagon loads needed to carry the logs.
  b Find the number of wagon loads to move
    i 100 logs   **ii** 150 logs   **iii** 250 logs   **iv** 400 logs.

What fraction of the shape is

a shaded

b unshaded?

a $\frac{5}{9}$ is shaded

b $\frac{4}{9}$ is unshaded

1 What fraction of each shape is shaded?

a

b

c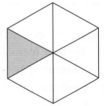

d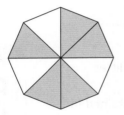

e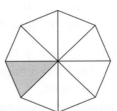

2 What fraction of each shape is **i** shaded **ii** unshaded?

a

b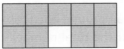

c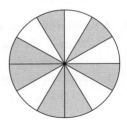

d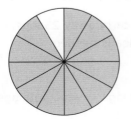

e

MyMaths.co.uk

Q 1220, 1370 SEARCH

Write the fraction of the shape that is shaded, in two different ways.

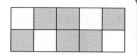

The fraction is $\frac{6}{10} = \frac{3}{5}$ Divide both 6 and 10 by 2.

1 Write the fraction of the shape that is shaded, in two different ways.

a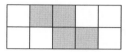

b

c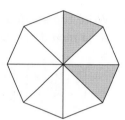

d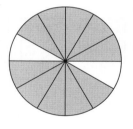

e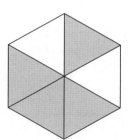

f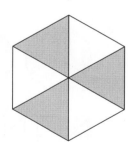

g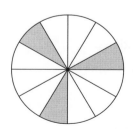

h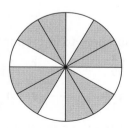

i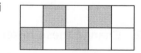

2 Write an equivalent fraction for each.

a $\frac{3}{15}$ **b** $\frac{5}{20}$ **c** $\frac{5}{25}$ **d** $\frac{6}{30}$ **e** $\frac{5}{40}$

a Change $1\frac{11}{12}$ to an improper fraction.

b Change $\frac{37}{10}$ to a mixed number.

---

a $1\frac{11}{12} = \frac{1 \times 12 + 11}{12} = \frac{12 + 11}{12} = \frac{23}{12}$

b 10 goes into 37 three times with 7 left over, so $\frac{37}{10} = 3\frac{7}{10}$

1 Write the shaded part of each diagram as

    a a mixed number   **b** an improper fraction.

a
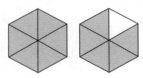

b
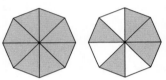

c

d

e

2 Change these mixed numbers to improper fractions.

    a $1\frac{2}{5}$ **b** $1\frac{4}{9}$ **c** $1\frac{5}{12}$

    d $2\frac{2}{7}$ **e** $3\frac{3}{10}$ **f** $4\frac{7}{10}$

3 Change these improper fractions to mixed numbers.

    a $\frac{8}{5}$ **b** $\frac{6}{5}$ **c** $\frac{12}{7}$

    d $\frac{19}{9}$ **e** $\frac{39}{10}$ **f** $\frac{38}{9}$

MyMaths.co.uk

Q 1019   SEARCH

Jean buys 18 eggs, but when she gets home she finds that $\frac{1}{9}$ of them are broken.

How many eggs are broken?

- -

The number of broken eggs is $\frac{1}{9}$ of 18 eggs or
$18 \div 9 = 2$ eggs

1 Calculate

a $\frac{1}{4}$ of 16   **b** $\frac{1}{3}$ of 27

c $\frac{1}{5}$ of 40   **d** $\frac{1}{7}$ of 49

e $\frac{1}{2}$ of 264   **f** $\frac{1}{6}$ of 42

2 Change the improper fractions to whole numbers.

a $\frac{39}{3}$ **b** $\frac{28}{2}$

c $\frac{65}{5}$ **d** $\frac{88}{4}$

e $\frac{36}{6}$ **f** $\frac{99}{9}$

g $\frac{72}{3}$ **h** $\frac{60}{4}$

i $\frac{105}{5}$

3 Mr. Brown weighs 84 kg. How heavy is

a Martin Brown if he is $\frac{1}{3}$ of his father's weight

b Sally Brown if she is $\frac{1}{4}$ of her father's weight?

4 The distance from London to Glasgow is 640 km.

Rugby is $\frac{1}{5}$ of the way.

How far is it from London to Rugby?

In class 7B there are 30 students. One day $\frac{9}{10}$ of them are present. How many students are present?

The number of students present = $\frac{9}{10}$ of 30

$\frac{1}{10}$ of 30 = 3

$\frac{9}{10}$ of 30 = 3 × 9 = 27

27 students are present.

1 Calculate these amounts.

    a $\frac{1}{3}$ of 18   **b** $\frac{1}{6}$ of 54   **c** $\frac{1}{2}$ of 28   **d** $\frac{1}{4}$ of 12

    e $\frac{1}{5}$ of 45   **f** $\frac{1}{7}$ of 28   **g** $\frac{1}{8}$ of 56   **h** $\frac{1}{3}$ of 39

2 Calculate these amounts.

    a $\frac{2}{3}$ of 6   **b** $\frac{3}{8}$ of 8   **c** $\frac{4}{5}$ of 10   **d** $\frac{3}{4}$ of 16

    e $\frac{3}{5}$ of 25   **f** $\frac{2}{7}$ of 35   **g** $\frac{4}{9}$ of 81   **h** $\frac{5}{8}$ of 56

3 Mr Lawrence weighs 75 kg. How heavy is

    a Mrs Lawrence if she is $\frac{2}{3}$ as heavy

    b Tom Lawrence if he is $\frac{3}{5}$ as heavy

    c Kate Lawrence if she is $\frac{7}{15}$ as heavy?

4 The longest river in England is the River Thames with a length of 335 km. The second longest is the River Trent which is $\frac{4}{5}$ as long as the Thames. How long is the River Trent?

5 The distance from London to Leeds is 300 km.

    a Doncaster is $\frac{5}{6}$ of the way from London.

        How far is Doncaster from London?

    b Retford is $\frac{3}{4}$ of the way from London.

        How far is Retford from London?

MyMaths.co.uk

Q 1018   SEARCH

A room has an area of 20 m² and 50% of it is covered by a carpet. Find the area of the carpet.

Area of the carpet = 50% of 20 = $\frac{50}{100}$ of 20
$$= \frac{1}{2} \text{ of } 20$$
$$= 10 \text{ m}^2$$

1 Find these amounts.

a 50% of £300	**b** 50% of £80	**c** 30% of £50
d 50% of £400	**e** 50% of £300	**f** 40% of £90
g 10% of 400 m	**h** 10% of 70 m	**i** 80% of 40 m
j 10% of 140 ml	**k** 10% of 150 ml	**l** 50% of 200 ml
m 20% of 270 cm	**n** 20% of 80 cm	**o** 10% of 362 cm

2 A football club has 30 players, but only 50% of them have ever played for the first team.
Find the number who have played for the first team.

3 At 10 a.m. a newspaper seller is given 350 papers and by 11 a.m. he has sold 10% of them.
Find the number that he has sold by 11 a.m.

4 On a bus 55% of the seats are occupied.
What percentage are empty?

5 91% of an iceberg is underwater.
What percentage is above the water?

6 In a train 25% of the passengers are sitting in first class seats and 10% are sitting in the restaurant car.
The rest of the passengers are in second class seats.
What percentage are sitting in second class seats?

The price of a bike is £180, but a dealer offers it for sale with a 25% discount.

Find **a** the discount

b the price paid by the purchaser.

- -

a The discount = 25% of £180 = $\frac{1}{4} \times 180$ = £45

b The price paid by the purchaser = 180 − 45 = £135

1 Find these amounts.

   a 10% of £1200

   b 20% of £1100

   c 30% of £150

   d 25% of 96 m

   e 75% of 44 kg

2 Find

   i the discount

   ii the price paid by the purchaser.

	Item	Marked price	Discount offered
a	Radio	£50	10%
b	DVD player	£80	25%
c	Washing machine	£190	10%
d	Television	£240	25%
e	Clothes drier	£160	20%

3 There are 90 students at a nursery school.

50% of them are four years old.

30% of them are three years old.

20% of them are two years old.

Find the number of students of each age.

MyMaths.co.uk

Q 1030   SEARCH

Write the fraction $\frac{32}{40}$ as tenths and then give the decimal and percentage equivalent.

$\frac{32}{40} = \frac{8}{10}$ Divide numerator and denominator by 4.

$\quad = 0.8$ $\frac{8}{10}$ is 'eight tenths.'

$\quad = 0.8 \times 100\%$ Multiply by 100%.

$\quad = 80\%$

1 Write each area A to H as a fraction of the area of the rectangle.
Write the fraction as tenths and give the decimal and percentage equivalent.
The first one is done for you.

Area A is 2 squares.
The big rectangle is 20 squares.
As a fraction: $\frac{2}{20} = \frac{1}{10}$
As a decimal: 0.1
As a percentage: 10%

 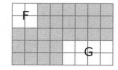 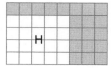

2 Write the area X as a fraction of the area of
the rectangle. Think carefully about giving the
decimal and percentage equivalent.

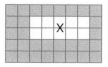

3 Give the decimal and percentage equivalent of these.

a $\frac{14}{20}$ **b** $\frac{12}{20}$ **c** $\frac{21}{30}$

d $\frac{18}{30}$ **e** $\frac{15}{30}$ **f** $\frac{36}{40}$

4 Give the decimal and percentage equivalent of these.

a $\frac{5}{50}$ **b** $\frac{35}{50}$ **c** $\frac{25}{50}$ **d** $\frac{60}{100}$ **e** $\frac{40}{100}$

MyMaths.co.uk

Q 1029   SEARCH

Which one of these angles measures 65°?

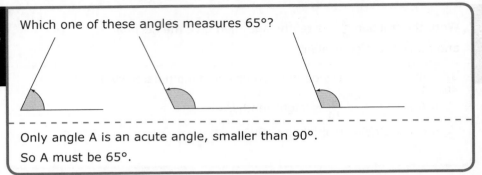

Only angle A is an acute angle, smaller than 90°.

So A must be 65°.

1 What kind of angle is each of these?

a

b

c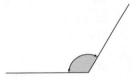

d

e

f

g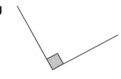

h

2 Match each item on the left with one on the right.

acute angle	180°
straight line	between 90° and 180°
full turn	right angle
obtuse angle	90°
quarter turn	360°
90°	less than 90°

3 How many degrees are there in

a a half turn **b** a quarter turn

c a three-quarters turn **d** a full turn?

Look at the diagram. Find the other
angle on the straight line.

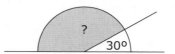

$180° - 30° = 150°$

1 Find the other angle on the straight line.

a

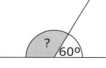

b

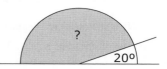

c

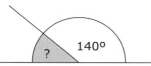

d

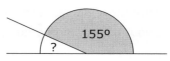

2 Find the other angle on the straight line for each of these.

   a 36°   **b** 65°   **c** 78°   **d** 153°   **e** 108°

3 Find each missing angle.

a

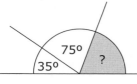

b

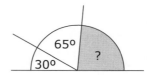

c

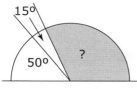

d

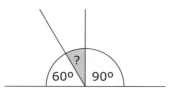

4 Find each missing angle.

a

b

c

d

Measure these angles.

a 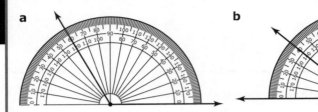 b

a Use the anticlockwise scale. The angle is 120°.
b Use the clockwise scale. The angle is 40°.

1 Measure these angles with a protractor. Write an estimate first.
Give your answer in degrees (°).

a

a

b

b

c

c

d

d

e

e

Find the missing angle.

There are 360° in a whole turn.
The missing angle is
360 − 220 = 140°

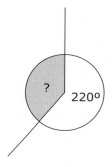

1 Find the missing angles.

a

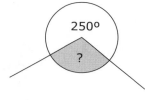

b

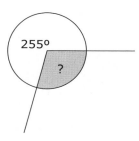

c

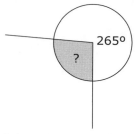

d

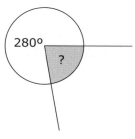

2 Find the missing angles.

a

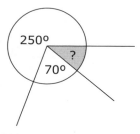

b

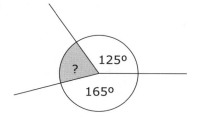

Find the missing angle.

- - - - - - - - - - - - - - - - - - - -

The right angle is 90°.
The known angle is 60°.
90° − 60° = 30°
? = 30°.

1 Find the missing angle for each of these.

a

35°

b

73°

c

24°

d

? 25°

e

99° ?

f

76° ?

2 What kind of angle is each of these?

a

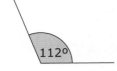

112°

b

294°

c

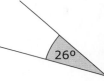

26°

d

128°

3 Find the missing angle for each of these.

a

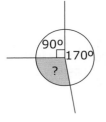

90° 170°
?

b

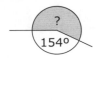

? 154°

c

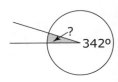

? 342°

Write the names of the triangles from their description.

a A triangle with no equal sides and no equal angles.
b A triangle with two equal sides and two equal angles.
c A triangle with three equal sides and three 60° angles.
d A triangle which has a right-angle as one of its angles.

- -

a scalene   **b** isosceles
c equilateral   **d** right-angled

1 State whether each of these triangles is equilateral, isosceles, scalene or right-angled. Explain your answer.

a

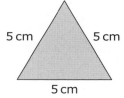

5 cm   5 cm

5 cm

b

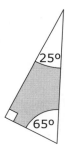

25°

65°

c

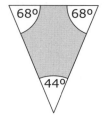

68°   68°

44°

d

3.3 cm   2.2 cm

4.5 cm

2 Choose two of these cards to classify each of these triangles.

(scalene)   (equilateral)   (isosceles)   (right-angled)

You may use each card more than once.

a

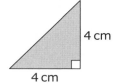

4 cm

4 cm

b

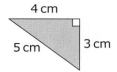

4 cm

5 cm   3 cm

Find the missing angle in the triangle.

The angles in a triangle add up to 180°.

$90° + 36° + ? = 180°$

$\quad 126° + ? = 180°$

$\quad\quad\quad ? = 180 - 126°$

$\quad\quad\quad ? = 54°$

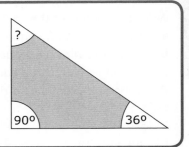

1 Find the missing angle in these triangles.

a

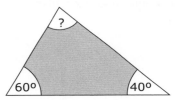

b

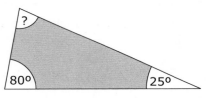

c

d

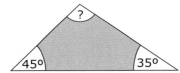

e

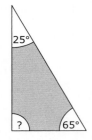

2 Find the missing angles in these isosceles triangles.

a

b

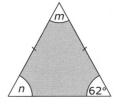

c

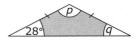

MyMaths.co.uk

Q 1082   SEARCH

Nick is facing east.

a He turns 180° clockwise. Which direction is he now facing?

b He then turns 90° anticlockwise. Which direction is he now facing?

a

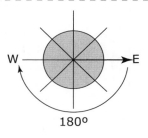

180°

b

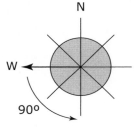

90°

There are 180° in half a turn.

Nick is now facing west.

There are 90° in a quarter turn.

Nick is now facing south.

1 Follow these coordinates.

Which direction are you going in?

a From A to B

b From B to C

c From C to D

d From D to E

e From E to F

f From F to G

g From G to H

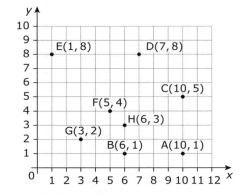

2 a Jennie is facing south. She turns 90° anticlockwise.

Which direction is she now facing?

b She then turns 180° clockwise.

Which direction is she now facing?

3 a Neil is facing north-west. He turns 180° clockwise.

Which direction is he now facing?

b He then turns 90° clockwise.

Which direction is he now facing?

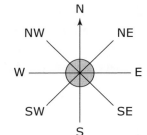

Give the coordinates of the points X, Y and Z.

X is at (3,2)   3 across and 2 up
Y is at (5,5)   5 across and 5 up
Z is at (6,4)   6 across and 4 up

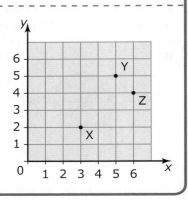

1   Give the coordinates of each point from A to W.

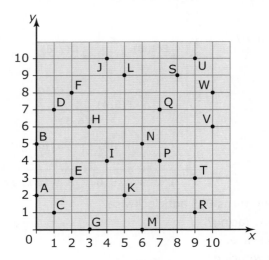

2   Copy the grid in question **1**, without the points.
Plot and label these points on your grid.

A(1,2)	**B**(3,3)	**C**(8,6)
D(2,9)	**E**(5,7)	**F**(6,3)

Example

Plot the points $(1, 2)$, $(-1, -2)$ and $(3, -2)$.

What type of triangle have you drawn?

Isosceles triangle.

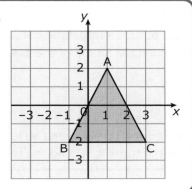

1 Plot the positions of each
   set of points on a copy of the grid.
   Join each point to the next with a
   straight line and suggest a name
   for the picture.

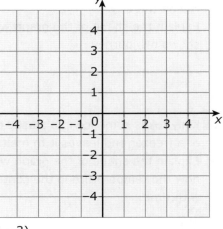

   a $(1, 10)$, $(1, 5)$, $(2, 4)$, $(2, -5)$,
        $(1, -6)$, $(0, -6)$, $(-1, -5)$,
        $(-1, 4)$, $(0, 5)$, $(0, 10)$, $(1, 10)$

   b $(1, 10)$, $(1, -1)$, $(2, 9)$, $(3, 10)$,
        $(4, 9)$, $(4, -7)$, $(3, -10)$, $(3, -5)$,
        $(4, -5)$, $(3, -5)$, $(3, 9)$, $(2, -1)$,
        $(2, -3)$, $(-1, -3)$, $(1, -3)$,
        $(1, -7)$, $(-1, -7)$, $(1, -7)$,
        $(0, -10)$, $(-1, -7)$, $(-1, -3)$, $(-2, -3)$,
        $(-2, -1)$, $(1, -1)$, $(-1, -1)$, $(-1, 10)$, $(1, 10)$

Sally fills a kettle, switches the power
on, but then forgets about it.
Explain the shape of the graph.

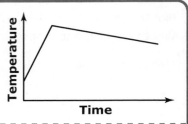

When the power is on the temperature rises very quickly, but the safety
switch turns it off and the temperature falls again very slowly.

1   Derek cycles from Westside Village to
    Eastside Village and passes over Tabletop
    Hill on the way.
    Explain the shape of the graph which
    shows his journey.

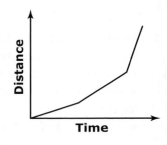

2   Kelly takes some ice in a plastic container out
    of a freezer and leaves it to melt.
    Explain the shape of the graph which shows
    how the temperature in the container changes
    with time.

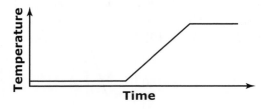

The graph shows Mr. Singh's journey to work by car one day. How far had he travelled by

a 8.45 a.m.   **b** 8.55 a.m.?

From the graph the answers are

a 6 km   **b** 10 km.

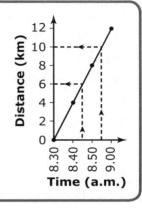

1 The graph shows Marlon's journey when he cycled to school one day.

a How far had he gone by
  i 8.30 a.m.
  ii 8.50 a.m.
  iii 8.05 a.m.?

b How long did it take him to travel
  i 10 km
  ii 5 km?

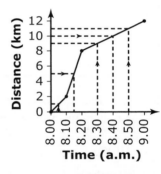

2 A small school has 240 students. The graph shows how many children had arrived at several times one morning before the bell went at 9.00 a.m.

From the graph, how many had arrived by

a 8.20 a.m.

b 8.30 a.m.

c 8.50 a.m.?

Students arriving at school

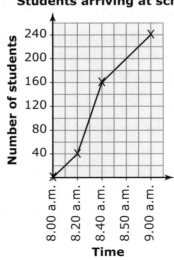

The table shows how many people were at a car boot sale at times between 10 a.m and 1 p.m. Draw a line graph of this data.

Time	10 a.m.	11 a.m.	12 noon	1 p.m.
Number of people	20	40	80	20

From your graph estimate the number of people who were there at 11.30 a.m.

There were about 60 people were there at 11.30 a.m.

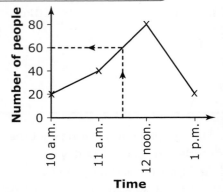

1 The table shows the number of people who were inside a football ground at half-hour intervals between 12 noon and 3 p.m.

Time	12 noon	12.30 p.m.	1.00 p.m.	1.30 p.m.	2.00 p.m.	2.30 p.m.	3.00 p.m.
Number of people	0	1000	2000	4000	5000	8000	10 000

Plot the data on a graph and use your graph to answer the questions.

a Estimate how many people had entered the ground by
   i   1.15 p.m.
   ii 12.45 p.m.
   iii 2.45 p.m.

b During which half-hour interval did most people enter the ground?

c How many people was this?

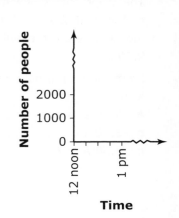

Use mental addition to find   51 + 36

- -

Count on from 51.
51 + 36 = 87

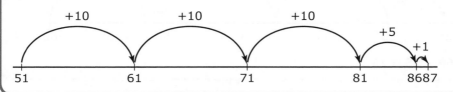

+10	+10	+10	+5	+1

51   61   71   81   8687

Work out these questions in your head.

1 Add 30 to these numbers.

   a 7   **b** 19   **c** 34

   d 52   **e** 85   **f** 105

2 Add 40 to these numbers.

   a 6   **b** 17   **c** 39

   d 55   **e** 87   **f** 108

3 Add 50 to these numbers.

   a 5   **b** 28   **c** 42

   d 69   **e** 83   **f** 104

4 Work out these.

   a 36 + 21   **b** 51 + 37   **c** 45 + 32   **d** 42 + 33

   e 46 + 19   **f** 59 + 25   **g** 65 + 28   **h** 58 + 34

5 Work out these.

   a 36 + 24   **b** 72 + 18   **c** 67 + 23   **d** 39 + 21   **e** 45 + 25

6 The distance from Newcastle to Durham
is 24 km and from Durham to Darlington
is 32 km.

What is the distance from Newcastle
to Darlington?

⊙ Newcastle

24 km

Durham

32 km

⊙ Darlington

MyMaths.co.uk

🔍 1345   **SEARCH**

Use mental subtraction to find 60 − 35.

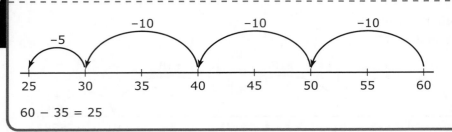

60 − 35 = 25

Work out these questions in your head.

1 Subtract 20 from these numbers.

   a 29   **b** 41   **c** 56   **d** 73   **e** 95

2 Subtract 40 from these numbers.

   a 48   **b** 62   **c** 83   **d** 102   **e** 150

3 Subtract these numbers from 30.

   a 19   **b** 21   **c** 18   **d** 12   **e** 15

4 Subtract these numbers from 60.

   a 29   **b** 19   **c** 31   **d** 11

   e 38   **f** 22   **g** 32   **h** 15

5 Work out these.

   a 55 − 21   **b** 63 − 41   **c** 96 − 42

   d 73 − 29   **e** 55 − 9   **f** 75 − 28

6 The distance from Leeds to Scarborough is 105 km, and from Leeds to York is 40 km.

What is the distance from York to Scarborough?

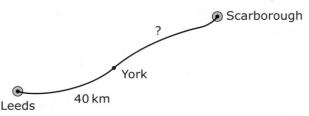

Use column addition or subtraction to calculate.

a 92 + 76   **b** 414 + 63   **c** 198 − 25

- -

a
$$\begin{array}{r} 92 \\ +\ 76 \\ \hline 178 \end{array}$$

b
$$\begin{array}{r} 414 \\ +\ 63 \\ \hline 477 \end{array}$$

c
$$\begin{array}{r} 198 \\ -\ 25 \\ \hline 173 \end{array}$$

1 Use a number line to solve these problems.

  a 32 + 16   **b** 42 − 16

  c 115 + 29   **d** 58 − 11

  e 548 − 137   **f** 244 + 83

2 Use column addition to solve these.

  a 51 + 41   **b** 65 + 34

  c 71 + 22   **d** 83 + 61

  e 91 + 52   **f** 115 + 42

  g 463 + 215   **h** 704 + 141

  i 155 + 122

3 Use column subtraction to solve these.

  a 69 − 44   **b** 87 − 23

  c 62 − 11   **d** 148 − 85

  e 127 − 52   **f** 197 − 144

  g 686 − 341   **h** 796 − 404

  i 999 − 622

4 Carla has £36 in her savings account.

Her godmother gives her £25 for her birthday.

How much does Carla have in her account now?

a Add together 350, 85 and 7

b Subtract 97 from 230

- -

a
$$
\begin{array}{r}
350 \\
85 \\
+\ 7 \\
\hline
442 \\
{\scriptstyle 1\ 1}
\end{array}
$$

b
$$
\begin{array}{r}
{\scriptstyle 1\ 2} \\
2\cancel{3}0 \\
-\ 97 \\
\hline
133
\end{array}
$$

1 Use columns to add these.

a	238 + 125	**b**	254 + 303	**c**	526 + 136
d	338 + 59	**e**	91 + 420	**f**	287 + 441
g	376 + 95	**h**	326 + 67	**i**	248 + 353
j	425 + 91	**k**	288 + 275	**l**	403 + 206

2 Use columns to subtract these.

a	428 − 217	**b**	533 − 31	**c**	632 − 112
d	562 − 138	**e**	764 − 125	**f**	473 − 48
g	454 − 26	**h**	563 − 138	**i**	674 − 246
j	479 − 55	**k**	555 − 282	**l**	633 − 148

3 Claire has 25 marbles, Jen has 43 and Marcus has 37.
How many marbles have they got altogether?

4 Sara is 118 cm tall. If she is 39 cm shorter than her mother,
how tall is her mother?

5 Mount Everest is 8700 m
above sea level and the
deepest point in the
Pacific Ocean is 10 800 m
below the surface. What is
the difference between
these two points?

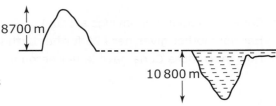

In a survey about school meals, one question was
'Which is your favourite school meal?'
How could this question be improved?

- -

You could list choices of the most common types of meal,
and add a box for 'other' This would make the data easier
to interpret.

1 Suggest any improvements that might be made to each questionnaire.

a In Jordan's class, maths homework is supposed to
take $1\frac{1}{3}$ hours per week. Jordan has given a questionnaire
to all students in the class.

How long do you spend each week on your
mathematics homework?

Up to $1\frac{1}{2}$ hours $1\frac{1}{2}$ to 3 hours   More than 3 hours

▢   ▢   ▢

b Marlon decided to ask everyone in his class how much fruit
they ate each day.

How much fruit do you eat per day?

Up to 1 kg   1 kg to 2 kg   More than 2 kg

▢   ▢   ▢

2 Rosie is doing a survey to find out which TV soap opera is most
popular with the students in her class.
Write a question she might ask.

James makes ten bus journeys to and from school each week. One week his journey times were 10, 9, 8, 10, 11, 9, 8, 10, 9 and 10 minutes. Make a combined tally chart and frequency table for this data.

Time (minutes)	Tally	Frequency
8	||	2
9	|||	3
10	||||	4
11	|	1

Total frequency = 10

For each question display the data on a combined tally chart and frequency table.

1 The table shows how many centuries a cricketer scored during each season of his career.

2000	1	2005	5	2010	3
2001	3	2006	4	2011	3
2002	3	2007	2	2012	4
2003	2	2008	3	2013	4
2004	2	2009	6	2014	5

2 Helen asked everyone in her class what pets they had.
Here are the answers she received:
dog, cat, cat, hamster, dog, goldfish, dog, cat, hamster, cat, guineapig, cat, horse, budgie, dog, mouse, budgie, cat, cat, dog, guineapig, dog, cat.

MyMaths.co.uk

Q 1235 SEARCH

Marcus needs 24 litres of white paint. Which is the cheapest way he can buy it?

Britewhite Paint	
3 *litre can*	£17.00
4 *litre can*	£22.50
5 *litre can*	£28.00

- - - - - - - - - - - - - - - - - - - -

8 three-litre cans cost
8 × £17 = £136
6 four-litre cans cost
6 × £22.50 = £135
5 five-litre cans cost 5 × £28 = £140
It is cheapest to buy 6 four-litre cans.

For questions **1** and **2** use this price list for Sam's Cafe.

1 One day Sam sold these numbers of sandwiches.
Tomato 25   Cheese 25
Beef 23   Ham 19
Find the money he collected from selling sandwiches.

Sam's Cafe		Price list
Sandwiches	Tomato	80p
	Cheese	85p
	Beef	90p
	Ham	95p
Ice Cream		90p
Ice Cream with fruit		£1.10
Tea		80p
Coffee		90p

2 One lunchtime Kanika, Josiah and Tanisha went to Sam's Cafe and their orders were these.
Kanika   One tomato sandwich, one ice cream and a tea.
Josiah   One cheese sandwich, one ice cream with fruit and a coffee.
Tanisha One ham sandwich, one ice cream and a coffee.
a Find the total bill for all three together.
b If they paid the total bill equally, how much did each pay?

The pictogram shows how many people visited a miniature railway on one weekend. Find the number of visitors on

a Saturday   **b** Sunday

Saturday	🙂	🙂	🙂		
Sunday	🙂	🙂	🙂	🙂	🙂

Key: 🙂 = 50 people

- -

a Number on Saturday = 3 × 50 = 150
b Number on Sunday = 5 × 50 = 250

---

1 The pictogram shows the number of children at a junior school.

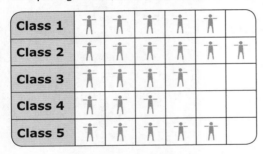

Class 1	🙂	🙂	🙂	🙂	🙂	
Class 2	🙂	🙂	🙂	🙂	🙂	🙂
Class 3	🙂	🙂	🙂	🙂		
Class 4	🙂	🙂	🙂			
Class 5	🙂	🙂	🙂	🙂	🙂	

Key: 🙂 = 5 students

a Find the number of children in each class.
b What is the total number of children in the school?

2 The pictogram shows how many trees woodcutters cut down in three weeks.
     a Find the number cut down each week.
     b What was the total number cut down altogether?

First week	🌲	🌲	🌲	🌲			
Second week	🌲	🌲	🌲				
Third week	🌲	🌲	🌲	🌲	🌲		

Key: 🌲 = 15 felled trees

3 Draw a pictogram to show the numbers of pairs of shoes a shop sold on each day of one week.

Monday 30	Tuesday 50	Wednesday 20
Thursday 30	Friday 40	Saturday 60

MyMaths.co.uk

Q 1205   **SEARCH**

The bar chart shows the numbers of people waiting at a bus stop.

a   How many
    i   men
    ii   women
    iii children are waiting?

b   What is the total number of people waiting?

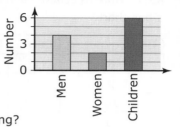

a   i   4   ii   2   iii   6   b   4 + 2 + 6 = 12

1   The bar chart shows the numbers of packets of crisps of four different flavours on a supermarket shelf.

    a   How many packets of each flavour are there?

    b   What is the total number of packets on the shelf?

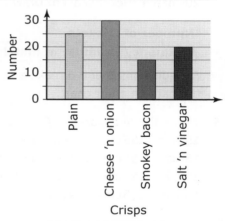

2   The pictogram shows how the boys in year 7 at High Lane School chose their winter sports options.

Football	🧍 🧍 🧍 🧍 🧍 🧍
Rugby	🧍 🧍 🧍
Cross Country	🧍 🧍
Hockey	🧍

Key: 🧍 = 10 boys

    a   How many chose each option?
    b   What is the total number of boys in the year?
    c   Draw a bar chart for this data.

3 The tally chart shows how long it took
Raj to walk to school each day for 2 weeks. Display this data on
a bar chart.

Time (minutes)	Tally	Frequency
8	II	2
9	III	3
10	IIII	4
11	I	1

Total frequency = 10

4 The table shows how many wickets a bowler took in each match of a
20-match cricket season. Draw a bar chart to show this data.

Number of wickets	0	1	2	3	4	5
Frequency (number of matches)	1	2	3	5	6	3

For questions **5** and **6** make a combined frequency table and then show
the data on a bar chart.

5 There are 24 children in Class 8B and their heights are:

152 cm	156 cm	153 cm	155 cm	156 cm	155 cm	153 cm
154 cm	155 cm	151 cm	153 cm	152 cm	157 cm	159 cm
157 cm	158 cm	157 cm	154 cm	153 cm	158 cm	152 cm
156 cm	150 cm	154 cm				

6 The pictogram shows the
number of people who
travelled on a motorway
coach service on each day
of one week.

Monday	🕴 🕴 🕴
Tuesday	🕴 🕴 🕴 🕴
Wednesday	🕴 🕴
Thursday	🕴 🕴 🕴 🕴 🕴
Friday	🕴 🕴 🕴 🕴 🕴 🕴
Saturday	🕴 🕴 🕴 🕴 🕴

Key: 🕴 = 3 people

MyMaths.co.uk

Q 1193, 1205 **SEARCH**

The pie chart shows how the people in a village voted at a general election.
What fraction of the people voted for each party?

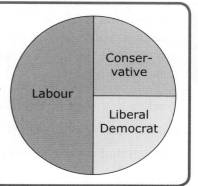

Labour $\frac{1}{2}$
Conservative $\frac{1}{4}$
Liberal Democrat $\frac{1}{4}$

1 The students in Class 7B have either dark, blonde or red hair.
The pie chart shows the fraction for each colour.
Guess the fraction of students who have
a   dark hair
b   blonde hair
c   red hair.

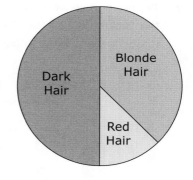

2 Camilla grows vegetables on her allotment. The pie chart shows the amount of space she uses for each kind of vegetable.
a   How many different kinds of vegetable does she grow?
b   What vegetable uses the most space?
c   Guess the fraction of the allotment that has carrots growing in it.
d   Which vegetable uses the least space?
e   Which vegetable grows in about $\frac{1}{4}$ of the allotment?

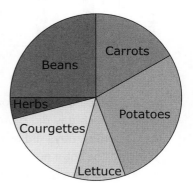

The pie chart shows what fraction of the passengers on a bus are going to three places. Write the fraction that are going to each place.

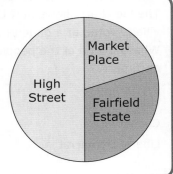

Fraction that went to High Street = $\frac{1}{2}$

Fraction that went to Market Place = $\frac{1}{6}$

Fraction that went to Fairfield Estate = $\frac{1}{3}$

1 Twenty people work at a small factory and every day they go either to the Tuckin Cafe or the Grubup Cafe for lunch. The bar chart shows how many of them went to each cafe on each day of one week.

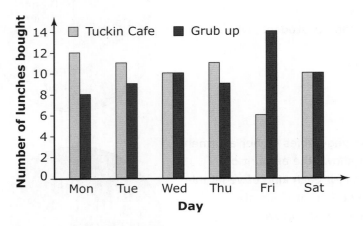

a On which days did more of them go to the Tuckin Cafe?
b On which day did more of them go to the Grubup Cafe?
c On which days did equal numbers go to both?
d Find the total number of lunches that each cafe served to the workers that week.

MyMaths.co.uk

1198, 1205, 1206 SEARCH

2 The pictogram shows how many people were waiting on each of the four platforms at a station one morning.

Platform 1	🕴			
Platform 2	🕴	🕴		
Platform 3	🕴			
Platform 4	🕴	🕴	🕴	🕴

a Find the number waiting on each platform.

b Find the total number of passengers waiting.

Key: 🕴 5 = people

3 The graph shows Kia's walk to school.

a How far has she walked by
   i 8.35 a.m.
   ii 8.55 a.m.?

b What is the time when she has walked
   i 400 m
   ii 800 m
   iii 600 m?

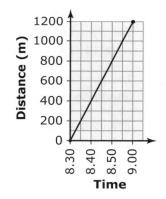

4 The pie chart shows the football teams supported by students at a school.

a Which is the most popular team?

b What fraction of the students support Spurs?

c Which team is supported by $\frac{1}{4}$ of the students.

d There are 240 students in the school. About how many support West Ham United?

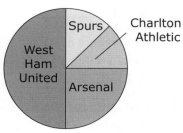

Asif got these marks for his geography homework.

4, 5, 5, 7, 7, 9, 7, 6, 8, 8 and 6

Find the mode for these marks.

- -

Put the marks in order: 4, 5, 5, 6, 6, 7, 7, 7, 8, 8, 9

7 is the mode because it has the highest frequency.

In questions **1–4**, find the mode.

1 The ages of twelve children who went on a skiing holiday were 16, 14, 15, 16, 15, 17, 15, 16, 15, 17, 16 and 15.

2 The numbers of England caps a footballer obtained each season over his fifteen-season career are 4, 3, 0, 5, 4, 5, 2, 4, 1, 0, 0, 2, 4, 1 and 2.

3 The list shows how many cars were sold at a garage on each day over a three-week period.

Mon	Tue	Wed	Thu	Fri	Sat		Mon	Tue	Wed	Thu	Fri	Sat
2	1	4	2	3	5		1	4	3	2	5	2

Mon	Tue	Wed	Thu	Fri	Sat
4	1	5	3	2	4

4 The numbers of students in each of the twenty classes at High Lane School are 26, 25, 24, 22, 24, 23, 26, 25, 23, 25, 26, 24, 25, 25, 22, 23, 23, 25, 24 and 23.

5 Jamila counted the numbers of different car colours in a car park.

red green white red blue black red silver silver
    white white blue red silver blue white black green
silver white white silver red brown white blue silver
    red white silver blue white white silver red white
blue white green silver

a Make a tally chart and a frequency table for this data.

b Which is the most common colour of car (the mode)?

Two dice were thrown eight times and the scores were
11, 6, 7, 6, 7, 5, 5 and 12.
Find the median score.

- -

The scores in order of size are 5, 5, 6, 6, 7, 7, 11, 12.
There is an even number of values.
The two 'middle' values are 6 and 7, so the median is $\frac{6+7}{2}$ = 6.5

1 A bus was late by these numbers of minutes on five days.

Monday	Tuesday	Wednesday	Thursday	Friday
5	7	9	1	2

Find the median member of minutes the bus was late.

2 Five school buses carry students to North Park School.
One day the numbers carried were 36, 40, 33, 31 and 25.
Find the median number carried.

3 The table shows how far I travelled in my car each day one week.

Mon	Tue	Wed	Thu	Fri	Sat	Sun
42 km	53 km	47 km	61 km	94 km	35 km	90 km

Find the median distance travelled.

4 A ferry made eight sailings one day. The numbers of passengers
carried were 21, 15, 9, 18, 14, 25, 11 and 17.
Find the median number of passengers carried.

5 a A small class at The Grange School has only ten students and
their heights are
120, 116, 117, 113, 122, 114, 121, 124, 112 and 117 cm.
Find the median height.

b The weights of the students in part **a** are
37, 35, 32, 33, 31, 38, 39, 40, 29 and 36 kg.
Find the median weight of these students.

Example

Julianne timed how long she waited in the checkout queue at two supermarkets. She recorded nine times for each one.

Supermarket A   60, 50, 70, 60, 40, 80, 60, 50 and 70 seconds
Supermarket B   30, 90, 60, 20, 100, 40, 60, 80 and 60 seconds
a   Find the mode and the range for each set of data.
b   Compare the waiting times in the two supermarkets.

- -

Arrange the data in order
Supermarket A: 40, 50, 50, 60, 60, 60, 70, 70, 80
Supermarket B: 20, 30, 40, 60, 60, 60, 80, 90, 100
a   For supermarket A, the mode is 60. The range is 80 − 40 = 40.
      For supermarket B, the mode is 60. The range is 100 − 20 = 80.
b   The modal waiting time is 60 seconds in both supermarkets.
      The time varies a lot more in supermarket B.

1   Find the range for each set of data
   a   11 29 51 24 22 48   **b**   17 23 15 36 18 15 19 21

2   During two weeks, Del recorded the times in minutes that his journey took by two buses.

	Monday	Tuesday	Wednesday	Thursday	Friday
Bus 1	25	31	31	45	43
Bus 2	46	43	39	46	41

   a   Find the mode for each bus service.
   b   Calculate the range for each service.
   c   Compare the times the journey takes by each service.

3   Candace timed how long it took for a taxi to arrive on six occasions from each of two taxi firms.
     Ken's Taxis   20, 21, 22, 20, 23 and 20 minutes
     Quik Cab   23, 19, 16, 29, 16 and 17 minutes
   a   Calculate the mode for each taxi firm.
   b   Calculate the range for each firm.
   c   Compare the performance of the two taxi firms.

MyMaths.co.uk

Q 1200, 1203   **SEARCH**

Copy the diagram.
Draw a line of symmetry.

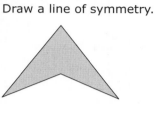
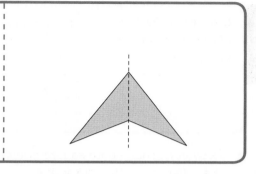

1 These shapes have only one line of symmetry.
Copy or trace each shape and draw the line of symmetry.

a **b**  **c** **d**

2 These shapes have more than one line of symmetry.
Copy or trace each shape and draw the lines of symmetry.

a **b** **c** **d**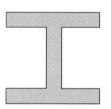

Draw the reflection of the shape in the mirror line.

Mirror Line

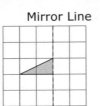
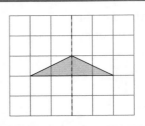

1 Copy each shape onto square grid paper and draw the reflection in the mirror line.

a
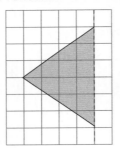

b
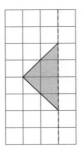

c
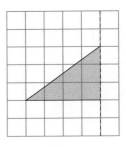

d
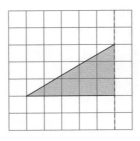

e
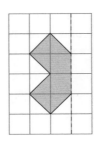

f
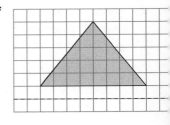

g
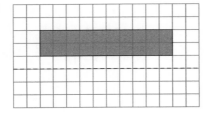

⊕ MyMaths.co.uk

Q 1114   SEARCH

Draw the image of this shape after the translation 3 right, 4 up.

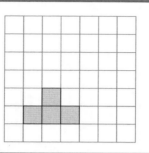

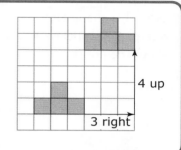

4 up

3 right

1 Describe the translation that will move the cross marked A to each of the positions B to K.

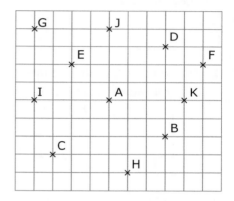

2 Copy this square near to the centre of a sheet of square grid paper. Draw the image of the square that is formed by each translation.

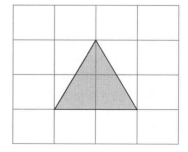

    a 8 right, 0 up   **b** 8 right, 8 down

    c 0 right, 8 down   **d** 8 left, 8 up

3 Draw this triangle near to the centre of a sheet of square grid paper. Draw the image of the triangle that is formed by each translation.

    a 8 right, 0 up   **b** 4 left, 7 down

    c 12 right, 7 down

Draw this shape after it rotates 90° anticlockwise about the dot.

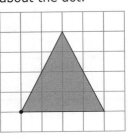

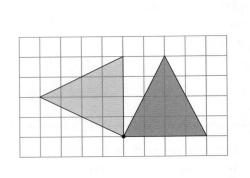

1 Describe each of these turns.
Use the words 'clockwise' and 'anticlockwise'.

a   b   c   d

2 a Copy this shape on square grid paper.
   b Rotate the shape 180° clockwise about the dot.

You can use tracing paper to help you.
   c Draw the rotated shape.

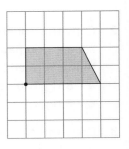

3 a Copy this shape on square grid paper.
   b Rotate the shape 90° anticlockwise about the dot.
   c Draw the rotated shape.

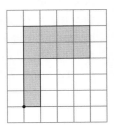

Copy this shape on square grid paper. Repeat it to make a tessellation.

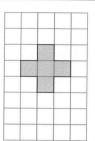
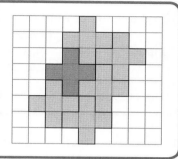

1   Copy each shape onto square grid paper. Repeat it to make a tessellation. Draw at least three shapes in each direction.

a
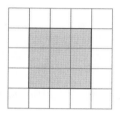

b
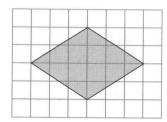

c
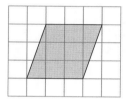

d
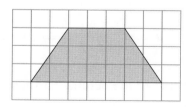

e
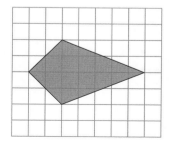

f
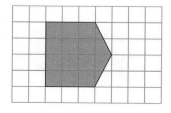

Find the output from the function machine if the input is 3.

Input : 3 ⟶ ×6 ⟹ +2 ⟶ Output = ?

The output is 3 × 6 + 2 = 18 + 2 = 20

1 Find the outputs for these function machines.

a
2
5 ⟶ ×5 ⟶
10

b
0
4 ⟶ +12 ⟶
13

c
18
19 ⟶ −6 ⟶
23

2 Work out the single function which changes these inputs to the outputs.

a 12 ⟶ ? ⟹ 15

b 12 ⟶ ? ⟹ 8

c 4 ⟶ ? ⟹ 20

d 30 ⟶ ? ⟹ 5

3 Work out the outputs for these functions.

a
4
5 ⟶ ×3 ⟹ +2 ⟶ ?
8
?
?

b
6
10 ⟶ ÷2 ⟹ +1 ⟶ ?
14
?
?

c
5
−2 ⟶ −3 ⟹ ×4 ⟶ ?
8
?
?

MyMaths.co.uk

Q 1159   SEARCH

a Draw the inverse function machine for this function machine.

b Find the output from the inverse function machine for an input of 5

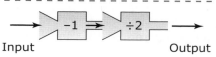

Input   Output

a Note that the operation figures are in reversed order and are of opposite sign.

Input   Output

b 5 − 1 = 4 and 4 ÷ 2 = 2 so the output is 2.

1 Give the inverse operation of each of these.

   a × 6   **b** ÷ 4   **c** + 10   **d** × 9

   e − 2   **f** + 3   **g** ÷ 8   **h** − 11

2 Draw the inverse function machine for each of these.

   a 2 ⟶ +6 ⟶ 8   **b** 9 ⟶ ×3 ⟶ 27

   c 12 ⟶ ÷4 ⟶ 3   **d** 8 ⟶ −1 ⟶ 7

   e 13 ⟶ ×2 ⟶ 26   **f** 23 ⟶ +4 ⟶ 27

3 For each of these, find the starting number by completing the inverse function machine.

   a ? ⟶ +6 ⟶ 8   **b** ? ⟶ ×3 ⟶ 36

       ? ⟵ −6 ⟵ 8   ? ⟵ ÷3 ⟵ 36

   c ? ⟶ −4 ⟶ 6   **d** ? ⟶ ÷5 ⟶ 3

       ? ⟵ ? ⟵ 6   ? ⟵ ? ⟵ 3

x students go to Charmaine's school. One hundred more go to Marlon's school.

a Use symbols to write an expression for the number of students at Marlon's school.

b 1300 students go to Marlon's school. How many students go to Charmaine's school?

- -

a x add 100 or $x + 100$

b $x + 100 = 1300$
The inverse of 'add 100' to 'subtract 100'
$x = 1300 - 100 = 1200$
There are 1200 students at Charmaine's school.

1 Calculate the values of these symbols.

a $a + 2 = 9$ **b** $b + 5 = 19$ **c** $c + 4 = 20$

d $d + 11 = 31$ **e** $3 + e = 12$ **f** $10 + f = 25$

g $11 + g = 32$ **h** $25 + h = 47$

2 Calculate the values of these symbols.

a $a - 2 = 6$ **b** $b - 7 = 10$ **c** $c - 11 = 3$

d $d - 8 = 9$ **e** $e - 14 = 8$ **f** $f - 9 = 16$

g $g - 50 = 110$ **h** $h - 53 = 27$

3 A coach can carry m passengers. The coach has 5 empty seats.

a Use symbols to write an expression for the number of people on the coach.

b There are 27 passengers on the coach. How many passengers can the coach carry?

4 A school hall contains n chairs. All of the seats are occupied and 5 people are standing at the back.

a Use symbols to write an expression for the number of people in this school hall.

b There are 55 people in the school hall. How many chairs are there?

MyMaths.co.uk

Q 1154   **SEARCH**

Find the value that makes this equation balance.

$2 + x = 4 \times 2$

- -

$2 + x = 4 \times 2$

$2 + x = 8$, so $x = 6$

Check: $2 + 6 = 8$

1 Find the value that makes each equation balance.

   a $n + 4 = 12$

   b $12 + x = 14$

   c $p + 17 = 23$

   d $y + 5 = 10$

   e $k \times 3 = 27$

   f $w - 6 = 17$

   g $r \times 8 = 24$

   h $19 - z = 12$

   i $v + 2 = 8$

2 Find the value that makes each equation balance.

   a $x + 6 = 2 + 4$

   b $5 \times 3 = n + 8$

   c $20 - d = 3 \times 2$

   d $11 + q = 10 + 6$

   e $x \div 2 = 5$

   f $8 \div x = 4$

   g $p - 14 = 18$

   h $m \times 3 = 2 + 19$

I think of a number and subtract 7. The answer is 9.
What number did I start with?

Write the missing number as n.

$n - 7 = 9$

$n = 16$

1 Use inverse operations to find the value of the letter in each equation.

   a $x + 25 = 40$ **b** $z + 72 = 104$ **c** $u - 8 = 33$

   d $9 \times n = 135$ **e** $q \div 5 = 17$ **f** $13 + y = 35$

   g $m \times 8 = 48$ **h** $17 - u = 9$ **i** $k \div 9 = 81$

2 A carpenter has a piece of wood of length 150 cm. If he cuts off a piece
of length 95 cm, what is the length of the remaining piece?

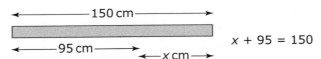

$x + 95 = 150$

3 A bottle contains 750 ml of lemonade and this exactly fills
five identical glasses. How many millilitres does each glass hold?

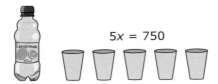

$5x = 750$

4 **a** I think of a number and add 5. The answer is 9.
     What number did I start with?

   b I think of a number and multiply it by 3. The answer is 18.
     What number did I start with?

   c Make up a puzzle like this of your own.

a What are the factors of 35?

b How many factors does 35 have?

- -

a $35 = 1 \times 35$ or 5×7

b So 35 has four factors: 1, 5, 7 and 35.

1 List the factors of

   a 6

   b 26

   c 8

   d 42

   e 56

   f 81

   g 36

   h 48

2 Which numbers have these sets of factors?

   a 1, 2, 5, 10

   b 1, 2, 3, 4, 6, 12

   c 1, 2, 4, 5, 10, 20

3 True or false?

   a 7 is a factor of 628

   b 5 is a factor of 255

   c 3 is a factor of 174

   d 8 is a factor of 753

What are the first four multiples of 15?

- -

The first four multiples are $15 \times 1 = 15$
$15 \times 2 = 30$
$15 \times 3 = 45$
$15 \times 4 = 60$

1 Find the first five multiples of 7.

2 Copy and complete the table to write the multiples up to
24 of each number 1–12. There is a column for each number
to help you organise.

Multiples of	The multiples up to 24																							
	1	2	3	4	5	6	7	8	9	10	11	12	13	14	15	16	17	18	19	20	21	22	23	24
1	1	2	3	4	5	6	7	8	9	10	11	12	13	14	15	16	17	18	19	20	21	22	23	24
2																								
3																								
4																								
5																								
6																								
7							7							14							21			
8																								
9																								
10								10												20				
11																								
12																								

3 From your table in question **2** find any numbers which are
multiples of both numbers in these pairs.
   a 4 and 5   **b** 6 and 9   **c** 4 and 10
   d 8 and 12   **e** 4 and 6

4 From your table in question **2** find any numbers which are
multiples of all three numbers in these trios.
   a 2, 3 and 4   **b** 2, 3 and 8   **c** 2, 4 and 10
   d 3, 4 and 6   **e** 3, 6 and 8

MyMaths.co.uk

Q 1035   SEARCH

Test to see if 135 divides by

a 2   **b** 3   **c** 5   **d** 4

- -

a It does not divide by 2 because it is not an even number.

b It does divide by 3 because 1 + 3 + 5 = 9 and 9 divides by 3.

c It does divide by 5 because its last digit is 5.

d It does not divide by 4 because the last two digits are 35 and 4 does not divide exactly into 35.

1 Copy and complete the table. The first three are done for you.

Number	Divides by 2?	Divides by 3?	Divides by 4?	Divides by 5?	Divides by 10?
150	✓	✓	✗		
153					
156					
165					
216					
360					
420					
630					
875					
996					

2 Mr Thomson has left £63,435 to be divided equally between his grandchildren.

Could the money be shared exactly between

a 5 grandchildren

b 8 grandchildren

c 3 grandchildren?

Use partitioning to work out 15^2.

- -

$15^2 = 15 \times 15$
$= (15 \times 10) + (15 \times 5)$
$= 150 + (10 \times 5) + (5 \times 5)$
$= 150 + 50 + 25$
$= 225$

1 Use partitioning or another method to work out these square numbers.

a	13^2	**b**	20^2	**c**	12^2	**d**	14^2
e	25^2	**f**	11^2	**g**	16^2	**h**	17^2

2 You can represent square numbers like this:

$2^2 = 4$ $4 = 1 + 3$

$3^2 = 9$ $9 = 1 + 3 + 5$

Draw diagrams like these to show

a 4^2

b 5^2

c 6^2

MyMaths.co.uk

Q 1053 SEARCH

Look at this cube. Find
a   the number of vertices
b   the number of faces
c   the number of edges.

a   8 vertices (or corners)   b   6 faces   c   12 edges

1   Look at these prisms. Copy and complete the table.

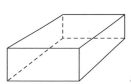
Cuboid
(rectangular prism)

Triangular
prism

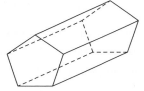
Pentagonal prism

Prism	Number of vertices	Number of faces	Number of edges
Triangular			
Cuboid			
Pentagonal			
Hexagonal			
Octagonal			

2   What are these 3D shapes?
   a   Circular base
       One vertex
       No straight edges
   b   Five faces
       Six vertices
       Nine edges
   c   Square base
       Four triangular faces
   d   Twelve edges, all the same length.

 **MyMaths**.co.uk

Fold this net to make a cube.

1 On square grid paper, draw three different nets of a cube.

2 Copy each of these nets onto square grid paper.
   Draw 'glue flaps' and fold lines.
   Cut out the net and fold and glue it to make a cube.

a

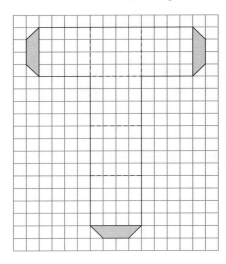

b

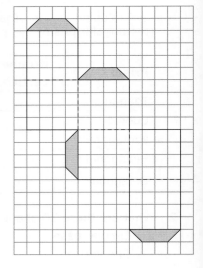

Draw a net of this cuboid.

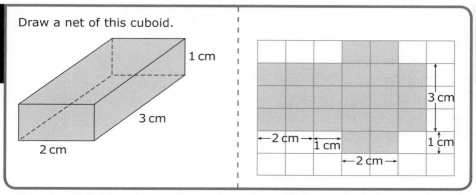

1 cm

3 cm

2 cm

2 cm → 1 cm

2 cm →

3 cm

1 cm

1 Draw a net of each solid on square grid paper.

a

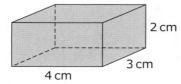

2 cm

3 cm

4 cm

b

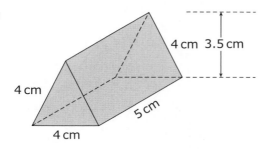

4 cm 3.5 cm

4 cm

5 cm

4 cm

c

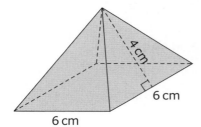

4 cm

6 cm

6 cm

Draw this cuboid
a from the front
b from the side
c from the top.

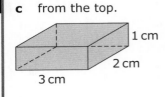

1 cm
2 cm
3 cm

a

3 cm · 1 cm

b

2 cm · 1 cm

c

3 cm · 2 cm

1 Draw this cuboid from
   a the front
   b the side
   c the top.

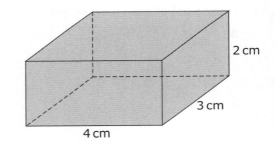

2 cm
3 cm
4 cm

2 Draw this prism from
   a the top
   b the front.

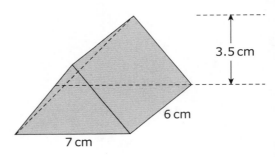

3.5 cm
6 cm
7 cm

3 Draw this cylinder from
   a the side
   b the top.

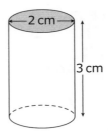

2 cm
3 cm

MyMaths.co.uk

Q 1098   **SEARCH**

When a stopwatch ticks from zero to 15 seconds, what angle does the hand turn through?

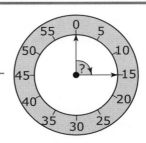

The angle 90°.

---

1 Look at the stopwatch in the example. Copy and complete the table to show the angle that the pointer turns through. Use a protractor to measure each angle.

Time	Angle (in degrees)
0 to 15 seconds	90°
0 to 30 seconds	
0 to 45 seconds	
0 to 20 seconds	
0 to 40 seconds	
0 to 12 seconds	

2 Draw these angles.

   a 40°   **b** 55°   **c** 70°

   d 120°   **e** 145°   **f** 180°

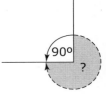

3 Measure each angle and match one of these cards with each angle below.

acute   reflex   obtuse   right

a   **b**   **c**   **d**

Construct this triangle accurately.
Measure the third angle.

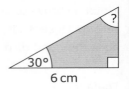

Draw a line 6 cm long.
Use a protractor to draw
the angles of 30° and 90°.
Join the lines.
Measure the missing angle:
? = 60°

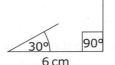

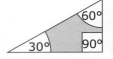

1 Construct these angles accurately.

a

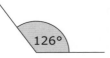

b

2 Construct these triangles accurately.
Measure the missing angles.

a

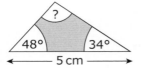

b

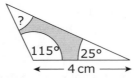

c

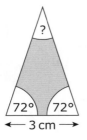

d

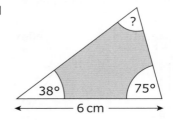

MyMaths.co.uk

Q 1090   SEARCH

a Use a ruler to measure the radius of this circle.

b What it its diameter?

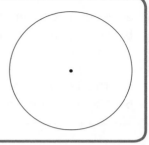

---

a The radius is 1.8 cm.

b The diameter is double the radius.
$2 \times 1.8 = 3.6$ cm.

1 Measure the

i radius and   **ii** the diameter of each circle.

a

b

c

d

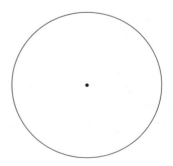

2 Kate has drawn this design.
Draw her design accurately.

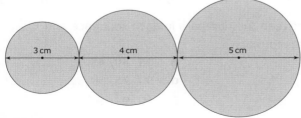

3 cm   4 cm   5 cm

a Find the difference between the numbers in this sequence.

b Find the next three numbers in the sequence.

11, 20, 29, __ , __ , __

- -

a The difference between the numbers is 9.

b The next three numbers are 38, 47 and 56.

---

1 Write each pattern as a number sequence. Give the first six terms of the sequence.

a    **b**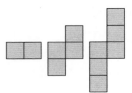

c 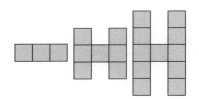   **d**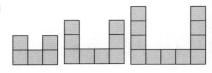

2 For each number line

i use the arrows to find the difference between the numbers.

ii find the next three numbers in the sequence.

a 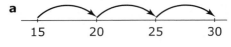   **b**

c    **d**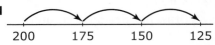

3 Find the difference between the numbers in each sequence and the next three numbers for each.

a 9, 12, 15, __ , __ , __   **b** 15, 30, 45, __ , __ , __

c 120, 100, 80, __ , __ , __   **d** 90, 75, 60, __ , __ , __

e 2, $2\frac{1}{2}$, 3, __ , __ , __   **f** 10, $9\frac{1}{2}$, 9, __ , __ , __

MyMaths.co.uk

Q 1173   SEARCH

Describe this sequence and find the next three numbers.

5, 20, 80, ___, ___, ___

- -

The rule is × 4. The description is Start and 5 and × 4.

The next three numbers are 320, 1280 and 5120.

1 State the rule and give the first six numbers for these sequences.

a 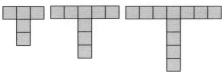   b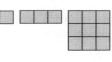

2 State the rule and describe these sequences.

a 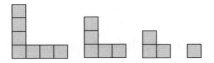   b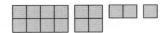

3 Match each sequence with its rules.

a Add 12		1000, 500, 250, 125
b Divide by 3		18, 30, 42, 54
c Multiply by 4		15, 60, 240, 960
d Subtract 15		1000, 200, 40, 8
e Divide by 5		2700, 900, 300, 100
f Divide by 2		85, 70, 55, 40

4 Find the first three numbers of each sequence.

- **a** ___, ___, ___, 4, 2, 1
- **b** ___, ___, ___, 900, 300, 100
- **c** ___, ___, ___, 105, 80, 55

5 Write a description for each sequence.

- **a** 3, 5, 7, 9, ...   **b** 5, 10, 20, 40, ...
- **c** 15, 11, 7, 3, ...   **d** 80, 40, 20, 10, ...

Write the first six terms of the sequence
'Start at 15 and +6.'

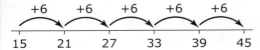

15   21   27   33   39   45

The first six terms are 15, 21, 27, 33, 39, 45.

1 Write the first six terms of each sequence.
  a 'Start at 2 and × 4'
  b 'Start at 15 and × 3'
  c 'Start at 36 and − 6'
  d 'Start at 1000 ÷ 2'

2 Peter is saving up for a moped which costs £2000.
  He only has £500, but he can save £250 each month.
  a Write a sequence to show how his money increases every month.
  b How long must he save up for?

3 Rajmeet is climbing Scafell Pike, the highest mountain in England
  which is 980 m high. She starts at 140 m and climbs up 168 m
  every hour.
  a Write a sequence to show how high up she is after every hour.
  b How long does it take her to get to the top?

4 Rapinda's mum has left 1200 ml of water gently boiling in a pan
  and 150 ml are boiled away every hour.
  a Write a sequence to show how much water is left after
    every hour.
  b How long does it take for the pan to boil dry?

Example

Draw three more arrows on this number line to show three more terms to the left. Write the sequence and give the rule.

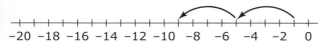

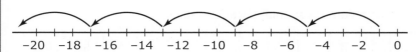

The sequence is −1, −5, −9, −13, −17, −21.
The rule for this sequence is 'Start at −1 and −4.'

1 Use the number line to help you find the missing terms.

a

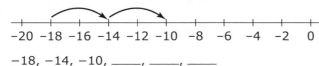

−18, −14, −10, ____, ____, ____

b

−28 −27 −26 −25 −24 −23 −22 −21 −20 −19 −18 −17 −16 −15 −14

−27, −25, −23, ____, ____, ____

2 Use the number line to help you find the missing terms.

a

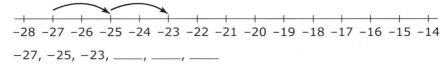

____, ____, −7, ____, −3, ____, ____

b

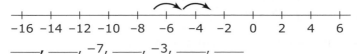

____, ____, −12, −8, −4 ____, ____

3 Janet has had to borrow £630 to buy a new washing machine and she repays £90 each month.
a Write a sequence to show how much she still owes after every month.
b How long does it take her to clear the debt?

MyMaths.co.uk

Chelsea has 4 friends. She gives each friend 3 sweets.

How many sweets does she give away?

- -

She gives away 4 × 3 = 12 sweets

1 Copy and complete these multiplication tables.

X	1	2	3	4	5
1				4	
2		4			
3					
4			12		
5					

X	6	7	8	9	10
6			48		
7		49			
8				72	
9	54				
10					100

2 Calculate these.

    a 3 × 6   **b** 7 × 6

    c 4 × 4   **d** 2 × 9

    e 8 × 5   **f** 10 × 9

    g 1 × 7   **h** 4 × 3

    i 6 × 6   **j** 3 × 8

3 A gardener can plant 6 seedlings in a seed tray.
How many seedlings can he plant in 8 seed trays?

4 Avril needs 2 eggs to make a sponge cake.
How many eggs will she need to make 9 cakes?

---

a Calculate 7.32 × 100

b Find the missing number in
84.2 ÷ ? = 0.0842

- -

a 7.32 × 100 = 732   The digits move two places to the left.

b 84.2 ÷ 1000 = 0.0842   The digits have moved three places to the right, so 84.2 has been divided by 1000.

---

1 Copy and complete these statements.

    a ☐ × 10 = 2.5   **b** 87 ÷ 10 = ☐

       0.25 × ☐ = 25   87 ÷ ☐ = 0.87

       0.25 × 1000 = ☐   ☐ ÷ 1000 = 0.087

2 Calculate each of these.

    a 14 × 10   **b** 5 × 100

    c 3 × 1000   **d** 5.2 × 10

    e 2.8 × 1000   **f** 4.36 × 10

    g 34.5 × 100   **h** 0.63 × 10

3 Calculate each of these.

    a 280 ÷ 10   **b** 5000 ÷ 100

    c 23 000 ÷ 1000   **d** 165 ÷ 10

    e 410 ÷ 100   **f** 52.7 ÷ 10

    g 1.9 ÷ 10   **h** 846 ÷ 1000

4 By writing each multiplier as two of its factors, calculate these.

    a 5 × 20 = 5 × 2 × ☐ =

    b 3 × 900 = 3 × ☐ × 100 =

    c 7 × 40 = 7 × ☐ × ☐ =

    d 11 × 500 =

    e 12 × 70 =

    f 15 × 400 =

Example

Work out 45×8 by using
 a partitioning
 b doubling and halving.

a $45 \times 8 = 40 \times 8 + 5 \times 8$
 $= 320 + 40$
 $= 360$

b $45 \times 8 = 90 \times 4$
 $= 180 \times 2$
 $= 360$

1 Use partitioning to find the answer to these.
 a 16×6 b 14×7 c 12×8
 d 24×5 e 9×33 f 58×4

2 Use doubling and halving to multiply these by 8.
 a 15 b 16 c 25

3 Use doubling and halving to multiply these by 16.
 a 7 b 5 c 25

4 Use doubling and halving to multiply these by 12.
 a 13 b 14 c 25

5 Eight school buses each carry 21 students to Northway School.
 How many students do the buses carry altogether?

6 Use repeated addition to work out these calculations.
 a 1.8×4 b 2.6×2 c 4.5×5

MyMaths.co.uk
1023 SEARCH

Example

Work out 112 × 6

An estimate is 100 × 6 = 600

112 × 6 = (100 + 12) × 6

= (100 × 6) + (12 × 6)

= 600 + 72

= 672

1 Use partitioning to work out these multiplications.

Work out an estimate first.

a 96 × 5   b 54 × 9

c 146 × 4   d 42 × 6

e 243 × 7   f 512 × 3

g 216 × 7   h 73 × 4

i 192 × 5

2 Use the grid method to work out these multiplications.

Work out an estimate first.

a 287 × 6

b 419 × 8

c 301 × 7

d 563 × 4

e 385 × 3

f 242 × 6

3 Nine paving stones are laid to form a path.

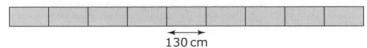

130 cm

How long is the path?

Work out $632 \div 10$

$632 \div 10 = 63.2$
The digits move one place to the right.

1 Use a number line to work out these division problems.
   a $42 \div 7$
   b $18 \div 3$
   c $45 \div 9$
   d $78 \div 6$
   e $85 \div 5$
   f $65 \div 13$

2 Divide each of these numbers by 10.
   a 30   b 70   c 160   d 820
   e 900   f 65   g 73   h 638
   i 402   j 209

3 Work out these division calculations.
   a $27 \div 3$ b $91 \div 7$ c $84 \div 12$ d $54 \div 9$
   e $48 \div 8$ f $44 \div 11$ g $64 \div 8$ h $50 \div 25$

4 An electrician has a piece of wire which is 48 cm long.
   If he has to cut it into 8 equal pieces how long will
   each piece be?

5 A greengrocer has 36 oranges which he places in packets of 4.
   How many packets will he fill?

MyMaths.co.uk

Calculate 170 ÷ 7

$170 ÷ 7$

$$
\begin{array}{lll}
170 & & \\
- \; 70 = 10 × 7 & & 10 \\
\overline{100} & & \\
- \; 70 = 10 × 7 & & 10 \\
\overline{30} & & \\
- \; 28 = 4 × 7 & & \underline{+4} \\
\overline{2} & & 24\,r\,2
\end{array}
$$

1 Work out these division problems.

   a 195 ÷ 5

   b 288 ÷ 6

   c 248 ÷ 4

   d 928 ÷ 8

   e 511 ÷ 7

   f 759 ÷ 3

   g 205 ÷ 5

   h 117 ÷ 9

2 Give the answer and remainder.

   a 53 ÷ 4   **b** 72 ÷ 5   **c** 92 ÷ 8   **d** 150 ÷ 7   **e** 100 ÷ 6

3 A supermarket manager is packing eggs into cartons of 6.

   He has 50 eggs.

   a How many cartons will he fill?

   b How many eggs will be left over?

4 53 students at Woodhill School are to be taken to a school football match in a minibus. The minibus can carry 9 students.

   a How many 'full' journeys will the minibus have to make?

   b How many students will be carried on the last journey?

Use repeated subtraction to calculate $147 \div 6$

$$
\begin{array}{r}
6)\overline{147} \\
-\ 60 \quad 6 \times 10 \\
\overline{87} \\
-\ 60 \quad 6 \times 10 \\
\overline{27} \\
-\ 24 \quad 6 \times 4 \\
\overline{3}
\end{array}
$$

$10 + 10 + 4 = 24$

Answer : $24\,r\,3$

1 Work out these divisions.

   a $70 \div 5$ **b** $72 \div 3$

   c $96 \div 4$ **d** $126 \div 7$

   e $210 \div 6$ **f** $180 \div 4$

2 Use a number line and repeated subtraction to calculate these.

   a $35 \div 4$ **b** $32 \div 5$

   c $29 \div 5$ **d** $86 \div 3$

   e $77 \div 6$ **f** $99 \div 6$

   g $52 \div 6$ **h** $75 \div 7$

3 Use repeated subtraction to solve these division problems.

   a $82 \div 4$ **b** $65 \div 3$

   c $102 \div 5$ **d** $234 \div 7$

   e $183 \div 6$ **f** $595 \div 9$

   g $411 \div 8$ **h** $136 \div 5$

4 114 people are waiting on a station platform and an empty train with 6 coaches arrives. If equal numbers of passengers sit in each of the coaches, how many are there in each coach?

MyMaths.co.uk

Q 1021, 1041   SEARCH

Calculate 29.1 ÷ 25. Give your answer to
a 1 decimal place **b** 2 decimal places.

- -

a 29.1 ÷ 25 = 1.164 = 1.2 to one decimal place, because
6 rounds up.
b 29.1 ÷ 25 = 1.164 = 1.16 to two decimal places, because
4 rounds down.

1 Round each number to the nearest ten.
    a 32   **b** 48   **c** 21   **d** 89   **e** 8
    f 35   **g** 167   **h** 153   **i** 536   **j** 109
    k 474   **l** 196   **m** 305

2 Round each number to the nearest one.
    a 3.9   **b** 8.6   **c** 7.3
    d 10.2   **e** 15.7   **f** 20.2

3 Write each number to one decimal place.
    a 1.37   **b** 5.63   **c** 6.28   **d** 7.85   **e** 0.92
    f 2.03   **g** 2.95   **h** 1.325   **i** 5.379   **j** 3.857

4 Write each number to two decimal places.
    a 1.543   **b** 2.617   **c** 4.285   **d** 5.971
    e 6.116   **f** 3.402   **g** 1.397   **h** 4.996

5 Use your calculator to do these divisions. Write each
answer to 2 decimal places.
    a 25 ÷ 3   **b** 55 ÷ 9   **c** 53 ÷ 9   **d** 47 ÷ 6
    e 86 ÷ 15   **f** 115 ÷ 12   **g** 35 ÷ 11   **h** 62 ÷ 11

6 Use your calculator for these problems. Express all answers in £ and p.
    a £9.06 + £6.34   **b** £7.27 + £10.51   **c** £12.36 − £7.03
    d £41.83 − £18.22   **e** £3.88 × 5   **f** £5.30 × 6
    g £1.29 × 4   **h** £8.66 × 15   **i** £5.24 × 16
    j £63.05 ÷ 5   **k** £93.45 ÷ 7   **l** £2.67 ÷ 3

In a group of 44 boys 20 were Arsenal supporters and
24 were Chelsea supporters.

a What is the ratio of Arsenal supporters to Chelsea supporters?
Write the ratio in its simplest form.

b What proportion of the boys support Chelsea?

- -

a The ratio = 20 : 24 = 5 : 6

b The proportion of Chelsea supporters is $\frac{24}{44} = \frac{6}{11}$.

---

1 Write each ratio in its simplest form.

   a 10 : 16

   b 15 : 24

   c 16 : 20

   d 10 : 25

   e 30 : 36

   f 18 : 27

2 On a camp site there are 12 caravans and 15 tents.

   a What is the ratio of caravans to tents?

   b What is the proportion of caravans?

3 At Holly Park School 15 girls chose athletics and 35 chose tennis.

   a What proportion of girls chose athletics?

   b What proportion of girls chose tennis?

   c What is the ratio of tennis player to athletes?

4 Tom is making a chicken korma.
He needs 700 g of chicken and 250 g of yogurt for the recipe.

   a What is the ratio of chicken to yogurt?
   Give your answer in its simplest form.

This recipe makes enough korma for 4 people.

   b If 8 people are coming to supper, how much

      i chicken

      ii yogurt will Tom need to buy?

MyMaths.co.uk

Q 1052 SEARCH

A school's string orchestra has 6 violin players,
2 viola players and 2 cello players
a What proportion of them are violin players?
b What is the ratio of violin players to cello players?

- -

a There are 10 players in all, so the proportion is $\frac{6}{10}$ or $\frac{3}{5}$.
b The ratio is 6 : 2 or 3 : 1.

1 Jimmy is waiting for a bus. He notices that 10 cars,
4 vans and 2 lorries pass the bus stop.
  a Find the proportion of the vehicles that were
    i cars   **ii** vans   **iii** lorries.
  b Find the ratio of
    i cars to vans   **ii** cars to lorries   **iii** vans to lorries

2 The display times for a set of traffic lights are:
Red 40 seconds, Red and Amber 5 seconds,
Green 25 seconds, Amber 10 seconds
  a Find the proportion of the total sequence that the
    lights are
    i red
    ii green.
  b Find the ratio of the Red display time to each
    i Red and Amber
    ii Green
    iii Amber.

3 The children in class 7C come to school by walking,
cycling or travelling on a bus. 12 walk to school,
4 cycle to school, 8 travel by bus.
  a Find the proportion of the class who walk to school.
  b Find the ratio of
    i walkers to cyclists
    ii bus travellers to walkers.

A boy's pencil case weighs 140 g when full and 35 g when empty.
If it contains 7 identical pencils, what is the weight of each
pencil?

- -

The weight of all of the pencils is $140 - 35 = 105$ g
So the weight of each pencil is $105 \div 7 = 15$ g

1 A school relay team complete a 4 by 100 m run in 51 seconds.
If the first, second and third runners complete their sprints in
12, 14 and 13 seconds, what is the last runner's time?

2 A van weighs 1935 kg when empty. It is loaded with 240 kg of
cement, 150 kg of sand and 600 kg of bricks. If the weight of the
driver is 75 kg, find the total weight which is moving.

3 In a new office building 45 doors are required. If each door is
fastened by 3 hinges, how many hinges are required?
What is the total number of screws required if each hinge
has 8 screw holes?

4 Tracey weighs 4 times more than her baby sister Emma.
  a If Tracey weighs 60 kg, how much does Emma weigh?
  b If their mother weighs 5 times more than Emma, how
    much does their mother weigh?
  c Their mother goes on a diet and loses 6 kg.
    How much does she weigh now?

A model ship is 50 cm long.
The scale used to build the model is
1 cm : 100 cm
100 cm.
Find the length of
the real ship in
both centimetres and metres.

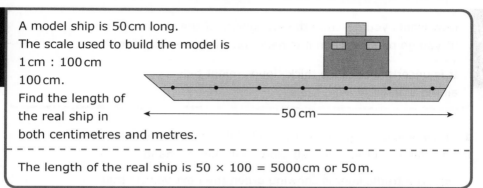

←——————— 50 cm ———————→

The length of the real ship is 50 × 100 = 5000 cm or 50 m.

1 A door on the plan of a house measures 2.5 cm by 1 cm.
The scale of the plan is 1 cm : 80 cm.
Find the real-life dimensions of the door.

2.5 cm

1 cm

2 On a plan, a garden measures 3 cm by 2 cm.

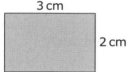

3 cm

2 cm

The scale of the plan is 1 cm : 1000 cm.
Find the dimensions of the real garden.
Give your answers in both centimetres and metres.

3 A doll's house is a scale model of a real house.
The scale is 1 cm : 15 cm.
If the doll's house is 100 cm long, 80 cm wide and
60 cm high, find the dimensions of the real house.
Give your answers in both centimetres and metres.

4 Measure the length of Green Park
Road on the map.
If the scale of the map is 1 cm : 2000 cm,
find the real length of Green Park
Road in both centimetres and metres.

Green Park Road

MyMaths.co.uk

Example

How would you describe the probability of the event,
'If you go outside when it is dark you will see some stars'?

It is uncertain because thick clouds might hide
all the stars.

1 How would you describe the probability of these events?

a Jake can touch his left elbow with his left hand.

b If a traffic light is showing green the next vehicle that
approaches it will go past it.

c If I throw a dice the score will be
i an odd number
ii an even number
iii a six.

d My dog will read this book.

e If you ascend far enough in a hot air balloon you will reach
outer space.

f Fred can balance his screwdriver on its blade.

g If I toss two coins the result will be
i a head and a tail
ii two heads
iii two tails.

h The month after May will be June.

MyMaths.co.uk

Q 1209   SEARCH

Jack is usually picked to play in about half of his club football matches. If I go to all the club's 30 matches next season, what is the probability that I will see him play at least 10 times?

Very likely, because he can expect to play about 15 times.

Impossible | Almost impossible | Very unlikely | Quite unlikely | Evens chance | Quite likely | Very likely | Almost certain | Certain

1 Jane throws two dice together. Describe the probability for each of these.
  a She will throw a double six.
  b She will throw any double.
  c She will throw any score up to and including 10.
  d She will throw any score which is less than 4.
  e She will throw a score of 1.

2 A newsagent sells the *Daily Chat* newspaper. They arrive at his shop at 9 a.m., but he has usually sold them all by 12 noon. Describe the probability that he still has some copies at each of these times.
  a 9 a.m.
  b 9.30 a.m.
  c 10.30 a.m.
  d 12 noon
  e 1 p.m.

3 If a meteorite crashes onto the Earth describe the probability of each of these.
  a It will fall on land.
  b It will fall on water.
  c It will fall in the northern hemisphere.
  d It will fall near the North Pole.

Look at this probability scale.

Impossible   Evens   Certain

Very	Unlikely	Likely	Very
unlikely	25% to 50%	50% to 75%	likely
0% to 25%			75% to 100%

What is the probability of the event
'If I go outside half an hour before sunrise I will find that
it is nearly daylight'?

- -

Very likely or 75% to 100%, because this would be so
unless it was very cloudy.

1   Suggest a probability for each of these events by using the probability
    scale. Give your answer as a percentage.
    a   If I go to the South Pole it might be raining.
    b   If my telephone rings it means that someone wants
        to speak to me.
    c   If you go to the Sahara Desert tomorrow you will see the sun.
    d   There will be a school holiday next week.
    e   If I draw a playing card from a pack it will be
        i   an ace
        ii   a club or a spade
        iii   an ace, king, queen or jack.
    f   If I throw a dice the score will be a number that divides into six.
    g   If you are at the North Pole you will be standing on ice above
        a frozen ocean.
    h   If I throw two dice together the score will be
        i   12
        ii   1.
    i   If I turn a light switch to its on position the light will come on.

MyMaths.co.uk

Q 1209   SEARCH

a Use a Venn diagram to sort the letters of the word 'FRACTIONS' into:

   the set of vowels   and   the set of letters in the word 'MATHS'.

b Redraw the Venn diagram using numbers to represent the number of letters in each region.

a

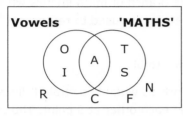

b

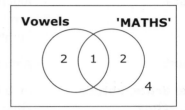

---

1 A warehouse uses a four-digit code for each item it stores.

The warehouse manager picks eight codes.

    X32C   Y23A   X11A   Z23B
    X12B   Z33A   Y13B   X21C

    a Sort the codes into each Venn diagram.

    i

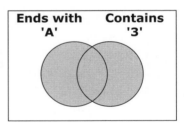

    ii Ends with 'A'   Contains '3'

    b Redraw the Venn diagram using numbers to represent the number of codes in each set.

2 Katya asks 20 students at her school if they are playing hockey or tennis in PE this term. Her results are shown on the Venn diagram. How many students are

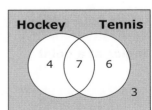

    a playing both hockey and tennis?

    b playing hockey?

    c not playing tennis?

    d Describe the shaded region in words.

add, addition (+)	Addition is the sum of two numbers or quantities.
adjacent (side)	Adjacent sides are next to each other and are joined by a common vertex.
algebra	Algebra is the branch of mathematics where symbols or letters are used to represent numbers.
amount	Amount means total.
angle: acute, obtuse, right, reflex	An angle is formed when two straight lines cross or meet each other at a point. The size of an angle is measured by the amount one line has been turned in relation to the other.

An acute angle is less than 90°

An obtuse angle is more than 90° but less than 180°

A right angle is a quarter of a turn, or 90°

A reflex angle is more than 180° but less than 360°

angles at a point   Angles at a point add up to 360°.

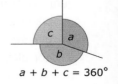

$a + b + c = 360°$

angles on a straight line	Angles on a straight line add up to 180°.

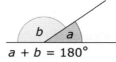

$$a + b = 180°$$

approximate, approximately	An approximate value is a value that is close to the actual value of a number.
approximately equal to (≈)	Approximately equal to means almost the same size.
area: square millimetre, square centimetre, square metre, square kilometre	The area of a surface is a measure of its size.
average	An average is a representative value of a set of data.
axis, axes	An axis is one of the lines used to locate a point in a coordinate system.
bar chart	A bar chart is a diagram that uses rectangles of equal width to display data. The frequency is given by the height of the rectangle.
bar-line graph	A bar-line graph is a diagram that uses lines to display data. The lengths of the lines are proportional to the frequencies.
base	The lower horizontal edge of a shape or solid is usually called the base. Similarly, the base of a solid is its lower face.

base

between	Between means in the space bounded by two limits.
brackets	Operations within brackets should be carried out first.

calculate, calculation	Calculate means work out using a mathematical procedure.
calculator	You can use a calculator to perform calculations.
cancel, cancellation	A fraction is cancelled down by dividing the numerator and denominator by a common factor. For example, $\frac{24}{40} \overset{\div 8}{\underset{\div 8}{=}} \frac{3}{5}$
capacity: litre	Capacity is a measure of the amount of liquid a 3D shape will hold.
centre of rotation	The centre of rotation is the fixed point about which a rotation takes place.
certain	An event that is certain will definitely happen.
chance	Chance is the probability of something happening.
class interval	A class interval is a group that you put data into to make it easier to handle.
common factor	A common factor is a factor of two or more numbers. For example, 2 is a common factor of 4 and 10.
compare	Compare means to assess the similarity of.
congruent	Congruent shapes are exactly the same shape and size.
consecutive	Consecutive means following on in order. For example, 2, 3 and 4 are consecutive integers.
construct	To construct means to draw a line, angle or shape accurately.

continue	Continue means carry on.
convert	Convert means to change.
coordinate pair	A coordinate pair is a pair of numbers that give the position of a point on a coordinate grid. For example, (3, 2) means 3 units across and 2 units up.
coordinate point	A coordinate point is the point described by a coordinate pair.
coordinates	Coordinates are the numbers that make up a coordinate pair.
data	Data are pieces of information.
data collection sheet	A data collection sheet is a sheet used to collect data. It is sometimes a list of questions with tick boxes for collecting answers.
decimal number	A decimal number is a number written using a decimal point.
decimal place (dp)	Each column after the decimal point is called a decimal place. For example, 0.65 has two decimal places (2 dp)
degree (°)	A degree is a measure of turn. There are 360° in a full turn.
denominator	The denominator is the bottom number in a fraction. It shows how many parts there are in total.
difference	You find the difference between two amounts by subtracting one from the other.
digit	A digit is any of the numbers 0, 1, 2, 3, 4, 5, 6, 7, 8, 9.

direction	The direction is the orientation of a line in space.
distance	The distance between two points is the length of the line that joins them.
divide, division (÷)	Divide means share equally.
divisible, divisibility	A whole number is divisible by another if there is no remainder left.
divisor	The divisor is the number that does the dividing. For example, in 14 ÷ 2 = 7 the divisor is 2.
double, halve	Double means multiply by two. Halve means divide by two.
edge (of solid)	An edge is a line along which two faces of a solid meet.
equal (sides, angles)	Equal sides are the same length. Equal angles are the same size.

edge

equally likely	Events are equally likely if they have the same probability.
equals (=)	Equals means having exactly the same value or size.
equation	An equation is a statement using an = sign to link two expressions.
equivalent, equivalence	Equivalent fractions are fractions with the same value.
estimate	An estimate is an approximate answer.
evaluate	Evaluate means find the value of an expression.
exact, exactly	Exact means completely accurate. For example, three divides into six exactly.

experiment	An experiment is a test or investigation to gather evidence for or against a theory.
expression	An expression is a collection of numbers and symbols linked by operations but not including an equals sign.
face	A face is a flat surface of a solid.

face

factor	A factor is a number that divides exactly into another number.

For example, 3 and 7 are factors of 21.

fair	In a fair experiment there is no bias towards any particular outcome.
fraction	A fraction is a way of describing $\frac{2}{5}$ a part of a whole.
frequency	Frequency is the number of times something occurs.
frequency diagram	A frequency diagram uses bars to display grouped data. The height of each bar gives the frequency of the group, and there is no space between the bars.
function	A function is a rule.

For example, +2, −3, ×4 and ÷5 are all functions.

function machine	A function machine links an input value to an output value by performing a function.
generalise	Generalise means formulate a general statement or rule.
generate	Generate means produce.
graph	A graph is a diagram that shows a relationship between variables.

greater than (>)	Greater than means more than. For example, 4 > 3.
grid	A grid is used as a background to plot coordinate points. It is usually squared.
height	Height is the vertical distance from the base to the top of a shape.
highest common factor (HCF)	The highest common factor is the largest factor that is common to two or more numbers. For example, the HCF of 12 and 8 is 4.
horizontal	Horizontal means flat and level with the ground.
hundredth	A hundredth is 1 out of 100. For example, 0.05 has 5 hundredths.
impossible	An event is impossible if it definitely cannot happen.
improper fraction	An improper fraction is a fraction where the numerator is greater than the denominator. For example, $\frac{8}{5}$.
increase, decrease	Increase means make greater. Decrease means make less.
input, output	Input is data fed into a machine or process. Output is the data produced by a machine or process.
integer	An integer is a positive or negative whole number (including zero). The integers are..., $-3, -2, -1, 0, 1, 2, 3, ...$
interpret	You interpret data whenever you make sense of it.

intersect, intersection	Two lines intersect at the point, or points, where they cross.

intersection

interval	An interval is the size of a class or group in a frequency table.
inverse	An inverse operation has the opposite effect to the original operation.
	For example, multiplication is the inverse of division.
label	A label is a description of a diagram or object.
length: millimetre, centimetre, metre, kilometre; mile, foot, inch	Length is a measure of distance. It is often used to describe one dimension of a shape.
less than (<)	Less than means smaller than.
	For example, 3 is less than 4 or 3 < 4.
likelihood	Likelihood is the probability of an event happening.
likely	An event is likely if it will happen more often than not.
line of symmetry	A line of symmetry is a line about which a 2D shape can be folded so that one half of the shape fits exactly on the other half.
line symmetry	A shape has line symmetry if it has a line of symmetry.
line	A line joins two points.
lowest common multiple (LCM)	The lowest common multiple is the smallest multiple that is common to two or more numbers.
	For example, the LCM of 4 and 6 is 12.
lowest terms	A fraction is in its lowest terms when the numerator and denominator have no common factors.

mapping

A mapping is a rule that can be applied to a set of numbers to give another set of numbers.

mass: gram, kilogram; ounce, pound

Mass is a measure of the amount of matter in an object. An object's mass is closely linked to its weight.

mean

The mean is an average value found by adding all the data values and dividing by the number of pieces of data.

measure

When you measure something you find the size of it.

median

The median is an average which is the middle value when the data is arranged in size order.

mirror line

A mirror line is a line of symmetry.

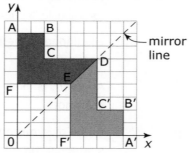

mixed number

A mixed number has a whole number part and a fraction part.

For example, $3\frac{1}{2}$ is a mixed number.

modal class

The modal class is the most commonly occurring class when the data is grouped. It is the class with the highest frequency.

mode

The mode is an average which is the data value that occurs most often.

multiple

A multiple of an integer is the product of that integer and any other.

For example, $6 \times 4 = 24$ and $6 \times 12 = 72$ are multiples of 6.

multiply, multiplication (×)	Multiplication is the operation of combining two numbers or quantities to form a product.
nearest	Nearest means the closest value.
negative	A negative number is a number less than zero.
net	A net is a 2D arrangement that can be folded to form a solid shape.
***n*th term**	The *n*th term is the general term of a sequence.
numerator	The numerator is the top number in a fraction. It shows how many parts you are dealing with.
object, image	The object is the original shape before a transformation. An image is the same shape after a transformation.
operation	An operation is a rule for processing numbers or objects. The basic operations are addition, subtraction, multiplication and division.
opposite (sides, angles)	Opposite means across from.
order	To order means to arrange according to size or importance.
order of operations	The conventional order of operations is BIDMAS: brackets first, then indices, then division and multiplication, then addition and subtraction.
order of rotation symmetry	The order of rotation symmetry is the number of times that a shape will fit on to itself during a full turn.
origin	The origin is the point where the *x*- and *y*-axes cross, that is (0, 0).
outcome	An outcome is the result of a trial or experiment.

parallel

Two lines that always stay the same distance apart are parallel. Parallel lines never cross or meet.

partition; part

To partition means to split a number into smaller amounts, or parts.

For example, 57 could be split into 50 + 7, or 40 + 17.

percentage (%)

A percentage is a fraction expressed as the number of parts per hundred.

perimeter

The perimeter of a shape is the distance around it. It is the total length of the edges.

perpendicular

Two lines are perpendicular to each other if they meet at a right angle.

pie chart

A pie chart uses a circle to display data. The angle at the centre of a sector is proportional to the frequency.

place value

The place value is the value of a digit in a decimal number.

For example, in 3.65 the digit 6 has a value of 6 tenths.

polygon: pentagon, hexagon, octagon

A polygon is a closed shape with three or more straight edges.

A pentagon has five sides   A hexagon has six sides.   An octagon has eight sides.

positive

A positive number is greater than zero.

predict

Predict means forecast in advance.

prime

A prime number is a number that has exactly two different factors.

probability

Probability is a measure of how likely an event is.

probability scale

A probability scale is a line numbered 0 to 1 or 0% to 100% on which you place an event based on its probability.

product

The product is the result of a multiplication.

proportion

Proportion compares the size of a part to the size of a whole. You can express a proportion as a fraction, decimal or percentage.

protractor (angle measurer)

A protractor is an instrument for measuring angles in degrees.

quadrant

A coordinate grid is divided into four quadrants by the x- and y-axes.

quadrilateral: arrowhead, kite, parallelogram, rectangle, rhombus, square, trapezium

A quadrilateral is a polygon with four sides.

rectangle   parallelogram   kite

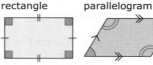 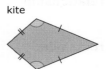

All angles are right angles.   Two pairs of parallel sides.   Two pairs of adjacent sides equal.

rhombus   square   trapezium

  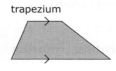

All sides the same length. Opposite angles equal.   All sides and angles equal.   One pair of parallel sides.

questionnaire

A questionnaire is a list of questions used to gather information in a survey.

quotient

A quotient is the result of a division.

random

A selection is random if each object or number is equally likely to be chosen.

range
The range is the difference between the largest and smallest values in a set of data.

ratio
Ratio compares the size of one part with the size of another part.

reflect, reflection
A reflection is a transformation in which corresponding points in the object and the image are the same distance from the mirror line.

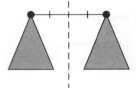

reflection symmetry
A shape has reflection symmetry if it has a line of symmetry.

regular
A regular polygon has equal sides and equal angles.

relationship
A relationship is a link between objects or numbers.

remainder
A remainder is the amount left over when one quantity is exactly divided by another.
For example, 9 ÷ 4 = 2 remainder 1 or 2 r 1.

represent
You represent data whenever you display it in the form of a diagram.

rotate, rotation
A rotation is a transformation in which every point in the object turns through the same angle relative to a fixed point.

rotation symmetry
A shape has rotation symmetry if when turned it fits onto itself more than once during a full turn.

round
You round a number by expressing it to a given degree of accuracy.
For example, 639 is 600 to the nearest 100 and 640 to the nearest 10.

To round to one decimal place means to round to the nearest tenth.

For example, 12.47 is 12.5 to 1 dp

rule

A rule describes the link between objects or numbers.

For example, the rule linking 2 and 6 may be +4 or ×3.

ruler

A ruler is an instrument for measuring lengths.

sequence

A sequence is a set of numbers or objects that follow a rule.

shape

A shape is made by a line or lines drawn on a surface, or by putting surfaces together.

side (of 2D shape)

A side is a line segment joining vertices.

sign

A sign is a symbol used to denote an operation.

simplest form

A fraction (or ratio) is in its simplest form when the numerator and denominator (or parts of the ratio) have no common factors.

For example, $\frac{3}{5}$ is expressed in its simplest form.

simplify

To simplify an expression you gather all like terms together into a single term.

sketch

A sketch shows the general shape of a graph or diagram.

solid (3D) shape: cube, cuboid, prism

A solid is a shape formed in three-dimensional space.

cube

six square faces

cuboid

six rectangular faces

prism

the end faces are constant

solution (of an equation)

The solution of an equation is the value of the variable that makes the equation true.

solve (an equation)
To solve an equation you need to find the value of the variable that will make the equation true.

spin, spinner
A spinner is an instrument for creating random outcomes, usually in probability experiments.

square-based pyramid, tetrahedron

pyramid

the faces meet at a common vertex angles equal.

tetrahedron

all faces are equilateral triangles

square-based pyramid

the base is a square

square number, squared
If you multiply a number by itself the result is a square number.

For example, 25 is a square number because $5^2 = 5 \times 5 = 25$.

square root
A square root is a number that when multiplied by itself is equal to a given number.

For example, $\sqrt{25} = 5$, because $5 \times 5 = 25$.

statistic, statistics
Statistics is the collection, display and analysis of information.

straight-line graph
When coordinate points lie in a straight line they form a straight-line graph. It is the graph of a linear equation.

substitute	When you substitute you replace part of an expression with its value.
subtract, subtraction (−)	Subtraction is the operation that finds the difference in size between two numbers.
sum	The sum is the total and is the result of an addition.
surface, surface area	The surface area of a solid is the total area of its faces.
survey	A survey is an investigation to find information.
symbol	A symbol is a letter, number or other mark that represents a number or an operation.
symmetrical	A shape is symmetrical if it is unchanged after a rotation or reflection.
table	A table is an arrangement of information, numbers or letters usually in rows and columns.
tally	You use a tally mark to represent an object when you collect data. Tally marks are usually made in groups of five to make it easier to count them.
temperature: degrees Celsius, degrees Fahrenheit	Temperature is a measure of how hot something is.
tenth	A tenth is 1 out of 10 or $\frac{1}{10}$. For example, 0.5 has 5 tenths.
term	A term is a number or object in a sequence. It is also part of an expression.
thousandth	A thousandth is 1 out of 1000 or $\frac{1}{1000}$. For example, 0.002 has 2 thousandths.

three-dimensional (3D)	Any solid shape is three-dimensional.
total	The total is the result of an addition.
transformation	A transformation moves a shape from one place to another.
translate, translation	A translation is a transformation in which every point in an object moves the same distance and direction. It is a sliding movement.

**triangle: equilateral,
isosceles, scalene,**

right-angled

A triangle is a polygon with three sides.

equilateral

three equal sides

isosceles

two equal sides

scalene

no equal sides

right-angled

one angle is 90°

two-dimensional (2D)	A flat shape has two dimensions, length and width or base and height.
unknown	An unknown is a variable. You can often find its value by solving an equation.
value	The value is the amount an expression or variable is worth.
variable	A variable is a symbol that can take any value.

vertex, vertices

A vertex of a shape is a point at which two or more edges meet.
The plural of vertex is vertices.

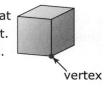

vertex

vertical

Vertical means straight up and down.

vertically opposite angles

When two straight lines cross they form two pairs of equal angles called vertically opposite angles.

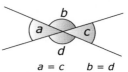

a = c   b = d

whole

The whole is the full amount.

width

Width is a dimension of an object describing how wide it is.

***x*-axis, *y*-axis**

On a coordinate grid, the *x*-axis is the horizontal axis and the *y*-axis is the verticalaxis.

***x*-coordinate, *y*-coordinate**

The *x*-coordinate is the distance along the *x*-axis. The *y*-coordinate is the distance along the *y*-axis.

For example, (−2, −3) is −2 along the *x*-axis and −3 along the *y*-axis.

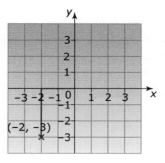

zero

Zero is nought or nothing. A zero place holder is used to show the place value of other digits in a number.

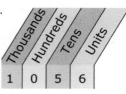